Seeds Of The Earth

A Private or Public Resource?

P. R. MOONEY

Published by Inter Pares (Ottawa) for the Canadian Council for International Co-operation and the International Coalition for Development Action (London).

Canadian Cataloguing in Publication Data

Mooney, P.R.

Seeds of the Earth

French edition: **Semences de la terre**

Spanish edition: **Semillas de la tierra**

ISBN 0-9690149-0-2 (English edition)

ISBN 0-9690149-1-0 (French edition)

ISBN 0-9690149-2-9 (Spanish edition)

Additional copies of all three versions can be ordered directly from the International Coalition for Development Action, Bedford Chambers, Covent Garden, London W.C. 2, United Kingdom.

Printed and bound in Canada by Mutual Press Limited, Ottawa.

ACKNOWLEDGEMENTS

Literally hundreds of people have been involved in this project. The working group would especially like to note the contribution of: Bob Scott and Ross Mountain in Europe; Gary Nabhan and Terry Murphy in the USA; Tim Brodhead (Inter Pares) and Nelson Coyle (CCIC) in Ottawa; Robert Morrisson, Graham Simpson, Lee Anne Hurlebert, Laurie Beingessner and Helmut Kuhn at the SCIC in Regina; and, Maureen Hollingworth, who edited the document. Special thanks should also go to The Graham Centre — in Wadesboro, North Carolina, USA — which has published Cary Fowler's unique and highly recommended *Seed Directory*.

However, this is very much an ongoing issue. We would welcome any comments, observations and/or contributions. Please write:

> c/o Pat R. Mooney,
> R.R. #1 Brandon,
> Manitoba, Canada.

Contents

Chapter 6

Restrictive Varietal Legislation   65

Chapter 7

Chapter 8

Chapter 9

Appendices

Foreword

Following the Fourth Session of the UN Conference on Trade and Development (Nairobi, 1976), where agricultural commodity issues dominated, the International Coalition for Development Action convened a small symposium for international food researchers in November 1977. This was held in the Qu'Appelle Valley near Regina, Saskatchewan in Canada. Long discussions led to the identification of a number of central food issues deserving broader international attention. High on the list of concerns was an issue identified simply as 'Seeds'; arising from a concern that the genetic base of the world's food supply was fast disappearing and that restrictive legislation was making it possible for agribusiness to gain control of this vital segment of the total food system.

The ICDA designated a working group to look at the 'Seeds' issue in December 1977. It included Cary Fowler from Chapel Hill, North Carolina in the USA — who first raised the issue and had already done considerable preparatory work; Jean-Pierre Berlan of Paris, France — who had attended the Qu'Appelle gathering and had offered substantial information on the European situation; Dan McCurry from Chicago, USA — another Qu'Appelle participant with extensive contacts among US farm groups; and, Pat Roy Mooney from Regina, Canada — who, as a member of ICDA's Co-ordinating Group, had arranged the Qu'Appelle session and had special responsibilities within the ICDA network for monitoring multinational enterprises.

Initial research revealed that restrictive varietal legislation — plant breeders' rights — was slated for Australia, Ireland and Canada in the near future; and that steps were being taken to expand the American legislation. Attention focused on Canada, where debate was imminently expected in Parliament. In March 1978, the Saskatchewan Council for International Co-operation — comprised of thirty international voluntary agencies in that province — presented a brief, "Food for People", to the Saskatchewan Cabinet which expressed strong opposition to the proposed legislation. Throughout 1978, the SCIC worked closely with ICDA's international group to develop a position on plant breeders' rights. By the fall, SCIC — in close conjunction with ICDA — produced a preliminary report titled *Genetic Resources and Plant Breeders' Rights,* which was widely circulated and became a source of intense debate in Canada and Europe.

Following ICDA's General Meeting in Geneva in October 1978, it was agreed that a more detailed study — international in scope — would be useful. The working group began a period of intense research co-ordinated through ICDA's Canadian member, the Canadian Council for International Co-operation, and closely supported by Tim Brodhead of ICDA's Co-ordinating Group. Pat Mooney of the SCIC was asked to continue to pull the material together and produce the study. *Seeds of the Earth* is the result of the combined work of these and many other people.

The paper continues to be heavily influenced by the Canadian experience with plant breeders' rights legislation. Throughout the fall and winter months of 1978/79, the SCIC organized scores of farmer-oriented meetings and symposia to debate the pending legislation. Many, if not all, western farm organizations in Canada adopted policy positions either opposed to PBR, or at least seeking more information about it. Political leaders in Ottawa were inundated with letters from protesting farmers and backyard gardeners, and a growing number of politicians expressed reservations about what had previously been viewed as simple 'housekeeping' legislation. Simultaneously, concern was growing within the scientific community about the loss of genetic material, and many respected scientists joined the call for more international action.

By February of this year, 'Seeds' had become a major farm issue in Canada. Over 500 farmers crowded into one assembly hall to hear a debate on the legislation between the Federal Minister of Agriculture and the President of the National Farmers' Union. The gathering registered almost unanimous opposition to the legislation. In mid-March, the SCIC, Saskatchewan universities and farm organizations convened a two-day conference on PBR, drawing in resource people from Europe and the USA. Once again, farmer opposition was clear, and key Federal Ministers began to express a willingness to reconsider the legislation or make adjustments for grain farmers. The spring Federal election meant specific debate on 'Seeds' was temporarily postponed; and as of this summer, the legislation has yet to be introduced.

During the course of several months of debate, both federal officials and the Canadian Seed Trade Association launched a major attack against the voluntary agencies — especially the SCIC — who were resisting the legislation. Government and seed trade officials challenged the right of voluntary agencies to speak about the issue and attributed a range of motives to their concern. Considering this issue directly concerns the Third World — not to mention the global implications — it appears to be well within the scope of normal NGO interests. In February 1979, the Board of Directors of the Canadian Council for International Co-operation unanimously passed a resolution calling for a world-wide campaign to conserve genetic material and for a halt to restrictive Canadian legislation.

This move demonstrated the extent of concern and breadth of support within the voluntary community on this issue. Similar legislation is still being drafted in Australia and Ireland, and the Canadian draft may be in Parliament in a few months. The ICDA is committed to raising the 'Seeds' issue at UN conferences and elsewhere, and hopes to share its research with Third World governments, scientists and farmers in the near future.

Richard Harmston,
CCIC, Ottawa,
August, 1979.

The Seed Situation

THE OLD CENTRES OF CROP DIVERSITY IN THE
THIRD WORLD ARE VANISHING . . . HOW SERIOUS IS
THIS PROBLEM? WHAT IS BEING DONE ABOUT IT?
DOES IT MAKE ANY DIFFERENCE TO GLOBAL FOOD
SUPPLIES? WHAT ARE THE IMPLICATIONS FOR THE
'GENE-POOR' NATIONS OF THE FIRST WORLD?

Chapter 1

The 'Gene-Rich' and the 'Gene-Poor'

If we had to rely only on the genetic resources now available in the United States for the genes and gene recombinants needed to minimize genetic vulnerability of all crops into the future, we would soon experience losses equal to or greater than those caused by southern corn leaf blight several years ago — at a rapidly accelerating rate across the entire crop spectrum.
— Dr. J. P. Kendrick Jr., University of California, Davis, USA, 1977.

1.1 Common Origins

Virtually everything people eat can be traced back to fewer than a dozen centres of extreme genetic diversity — the so-called 'Vavilov Centres', named after the great Russian scientist who dominated botany in the 1920s.[1] Following years of exploration, N. I. Vavilov concluded that a combination of varied topography, climate and cultivation methods resulted in almost all major crops originating on less than one-quarter of the earth's arable land. The major areas are the Mediterranean, the Near East, Afghanistan, Indo-Burma, Malaysia-Java, China, Guatemala-Mexico, the Peruvian Andes and Ethiopia.[2]

With the exception of a small area around the Mediterranean, the industrialized world is excluded from the centres of diversity. The reason for this botanical poverty stems from the time of the ice age; i.e. while the vegetative assets of the temperate zones were frozen, the tropical climes flourished in genetic diversity. The resulting differences in plant life would be difficult to exaggerate. Dr. Norman Myers of Nairobi tells of one small Philippino volcano, Mount Makiliang, which has growing on its slopes more woody plant species than are found in the whole of Canada. The Amazon River contains eight times as many living species as the Mississippi system and ten times as many as are in all of Europe.[3]

Fewer than 10% of the earth's 300,000 higher-order plants have benefited from even the most cursory scientific examination. Less than 3,000 have been studied in detail.[4] Ninety-five percent of human nutrition is derived from no more than 30 plants, eight of which comprise three-quarters of the plant kingdom's contribution to human energy. Three crops — wheat, rice and maize — account for over 75% of our cereal consumption.[5] This is not as it

3

Map 1
Vavilov Centres

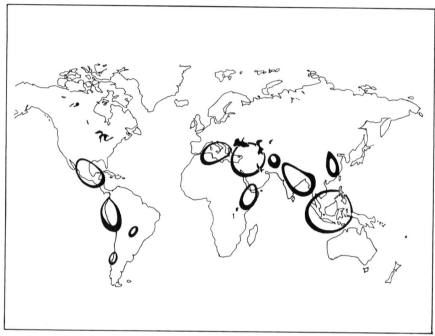

Source: *Genetic Conservation*. FAO Genetic Conservation Training Programme, Crop Ecology and Genetic Resources Unit, FAO, PI/F7460.

has always been. Prehistoric peoples found food in over 1,500 species of wild plants, and at least 500 major vegetables were used in ancient cultivation. In the space of a thousand years, our vegetable food diversity has narrowed to the 200 species grown by backyard gardeners and the 80 species favoured by market gardeners. Only 20 vegetable species are used in field cultivation.[6] Modern agricultural history is, at least in part, a history of declining food variety, as more and more people are nourished by fewer and fewer of the world's plant species.[7]

The result is a stunning degree of food interdependence. All of us look to common genetic pools for our food security; particularly Oceania and North America, which rely heavily on the genetic resources of the Third World. For example, the President of Agricultural Sciences at the University of California, Dr. J.P. Kendrick Jr., introduced a special issue of *California Agriculture* with the comment that of his state's 200 commercially-grown crops, none are native to California. In fact, of the 1,000 major crops harvested each year in North America, only Jerusalem artichokes, sunflowers and cranberries can properly claim this continent as home.[8]

Subsistent farmers in the Third World have been cultivating today's major food crops for over ten thousand years. By observing the natural process of mutation and by careful seed selection over the centuries, these

4

farmers have developed an astonishing range of crop variability.[9] This diversity has been necessary for survival. No one wheat or rice variety can provide adequate protection against monsoon failures, pests, rusts or blights. Practical farmers welcome a dozen or more varieties of wheat to their fields, because come drought, flood or rust, something will make it to harvest time. Despite recent impressive advances in genetic engineering, most agronomists would continue to argue that science cannot begin to match the variability of nature, and that no adequate technological replacement exists for the Vavilov Centres. Even the International Atomic Energy Agency, in its 1971 report, advised that induced germ plasm mutations through radiation is no alternative to the conservation and screening of natural germ plasm sources.[10]

No one source exists, or is commonly agreed upon, as fully identifying the first home of each major crop. Indeed, the origin of a crop and its actual centre of diversity may not always be one. Plants sometimes do better in an adopted home than in their original habitat. Nevertheless, Table 1 provides a crude summary of the original centres for key world crops. In the end, however, the genetic 'home' of a major crop might best be identified by the area in which ancient farmers have been most successful cultivating.

Table 1
World Crops: Origins

CROP	MAJOR CENTRE	CROP	MAJOR CENTRE
GRAINS:		Cauliflower	Mediterranean
Alfalfa	Asia Minor	Common Bean	Central America
Barley	Asia Minor	Cucumber	Indo-Burma
	Ethiopia		Malaysia
Broomcorn Millet	Central Asia	Eggplant	Indo-Burma
Buckwheat	China		China
Corn	Central America		Africa
	Andes	Garlic	Central Asia
Flax	Ethiopia		Asia Minor
	Asia Minor	Lettuce	Mediterranean
Foxtail Millet	Southeast Asia	Lima Bean	South America
Mustard	Central Asia	Onion	Ethiopia
Oats	Asia Minor		Central Asia
	Mediterranean		Asia Minor
Rice	West Africa	Parsnip	Mediterranean
	Indo-Burma	Pea	Asia Minor
	Southeast Asia		Central Asia
Rye	Asia Minor	Potato	Andes
Wheat	Ethiopia	Radish	China
	Asia Minor	Spinach	Central Asia
VEGETABLES:		Squash	Central America
Asparagus	Mediterranean		Andes
Beet	Asia Minor	Tomato	Central America
Broad Bean	Central Asia		Andes
Broccoli	Mediterranean	Turnip	Mediterranean
Cabbage	Asia Minor	Winged Bean	Papua New Guinea
	Mediterranean		
Carrot	Central Asia		
	Asia Minor		

Continued . . .

Table 1 (cont'd)
World Crops: Origins

CROP	MAJOR CENTRE	CROP	MAJOR CENTRE
FRUITS & NUTS:			
Almond	Asia Minor	Pomegranate	Asia Minor
	China	Pumpkin	Central America
Apple	Central Asia		South America
Apricot	Central Asia	Pineapple	Central America
	China		Brazil/Uruguay
Banana	Ethiopia	Rhubarb	Mediterranean
	Southeast Asia		China
Brazilnut	Brazil/Uruguay	Sesame	Ethiopia
Cherry	Asia Minor		Central Asia
	China/Japan	Strawberries	Southern Chile
Coconut	Southeast Asia	Sugar Cane	Indo-Burma
Date Palm	Asia Minor		Southeast Asia
Fig	Asia Minor		China
Grape	Central Asia	Sugar Beet	Europe
	Asia Minor	Watermelon	Central Asia
Grapefruit	Southeast Asia		
Lemon	Indo-Burma	**MISCELLANEOUS:**	
Melon	Central Asia	Cacao	Central America
	Indo-Burma	Carob	Mediterranean
Mango	Indo-Burma	Chicory	Mediterranean
Olive	Mediterranean	Coffee	Ethiopia
	Asia Minor	Cotton	Central Asia
Orange	China		Indo-Burma
	Indo-Burma		Central America
	Southeast Asia		South America
Papaya	Central America	Hemp	Central Asia
	Andes		Indo-Burma
Peach	China	Jute	Indo-Burma
Pear	Asia Minor	Sisal	Central America
	Central Asia	Tobacco	Central America
Peanut	Brazil/Uruguay	Tea	China

Sources: Information was gathered from a variety of botanical encyclopedias but key sources were the IBPGR publications and an agricultural map reference prepared at the Sorbonne in Paris.

Throughout history, every subsistent farmer has been an aggressive plant breeder. A modern tendency among some plant breeders to downgrade the historic contributions of Third World farmers is disappointing. Among those most experienced in international collections, Dr. Jack Harlan of the University of Illinois and Dr. Garrison Wilkes of the University of Massachusetts have been struck by the planned approach to seed collection taken by traditional cultivators.[11] Governments have also been involved for literally thousands of years. The first known international expedition, launched in 1570 B.C. by Egypt's Queen Hatshepsut, was to the Land of Punt (Somalia) in search of frankincense.[12] As far back as the eleventh century, Sung emperors in China were breeding early-maturing rice — imported from Indo-Burma — and had reduced the required growing season from 180 to 100 days. A century and a half ago, Chinese plant breeders had reduced the rice growing season to 35 days (after transplanting); and several varieties of short-stemmed rice were in the process of being developed.[13]

1.2 The Degree of Interdependence

The world's crop interdependence might best be shown in a story told about wheat by Dr. Jack Harlan: "The source could be traced from Galicia in Poland to Germany to Scotland to Canada where a single selection by David Fife of Ontario produced 'Red Fife'. It was C.E. Saunders, also of Canada, who crossed 'Red Fife' and 'Hard Red Calcutta' from India, and selected 'Marquis'."[14] The Canadian prairies could never have been a world breadbasket were it not for the turn-of-the-century introduction of 'Marquis' wheat. Last year, Canada's wheat farmers seeded over 55% of their fields in another variety — 'Neepawa' — containing an introduction known as 'Kenyan Farmer'. In total, 76% of prairie bread wheat is now at least partially derived from this East African introduction.[15] Nor is this situation unique to wheat. Canada's 'Harmon' oats contain genes from Egypt, Siberia and France; and, 'Bonanza' barley draws from Manchuria, Turkey and Finland.

In the early 1970s, the US Department of Agriculture (USDA) provided the public with a brief run-down of North America's dependence upon Third World germ plasm.[16] Cucumbers, for example, now depend heavily upon introductions from Korea, Burma and India.[17] Canada particularly depends upon three breeding lines from Burma. Canada's 'Butterking' lettuce traces back to Israel, while many American varieties look to Turkey.[18] The common bean grown in the USA contains disease-resistant traits from Mexico, Syria, Turkey, Chile and El Salvador.[19] Disease-resistance in peas, on the other hand, comes to North America from Peru, Iran, Turkey, Greece and Italy. As the USDA reported: "In response to urgent demands from industry", exploration teams combed the world in 1969-70 looking for peas carrying resistance to cold, drought and disease.[20] The same report noted that the US spinach industry "has been rescued repeatedly" from disaster through new introductions from India, Iran, Turkey, Manchuria and Belgium. For example, 'P.I. 140467' from Iran, is the basis for disease-resistance in the Californian spinach crop.[21]

It is not so much that Third World farmers have bred for diseases endemic to Australia or North America, as it is that the limited genetic base of Western nations provides little chance for disease-resistance. New genetic material is needed to continue the fight against constantly mutating pests and pathogens; material which does not only come from the original 'centres'.[22] Australia, for example, has made a significant contribution to the North American tomato industry although the centre of diversity is in Mexico. US tomatoes have also benefited by genes from Russia and Puerto Rico.[23] The bacterial wilt in Virginia tobacco has finally been blocked by an introduction from Colombia[24]; and that lush Bermuda grass decorating our lawns, golf courses and cemeteries is from South Africa.[25]

Our major cereal crops are particularly illustrative of the weakness of North America's genetic base. In 1973, researchers at Purdue University found the requirement they needed for sorghum in two introductions from Ethiopia.[26] If it were not for 'P.I. 178383', a wheat brought to the Pacific Northwest by Harlan from Turkey in 1948, US wheat farmers would lose at least another US $3 million a year to stripe rust.[27] Similarly, alfalfa variety 'AWPX3' traces to 32 clones from nine countries, including Saudi Arabia and Afghanistan.[28] When rust attacked the prairie oat crop in Canada a few years ago, University of Manitoba scientists found relief in new material from North Africa.[29]

Table 2
Sources of US Germ Plasm

CROP	MAIN SOURCES OF US GERM PLASM
Corn	Indigenous flints and dents, *in situ* development
Soybean	North and East China, Korea, Japan
Alfalfa	Chile, Germany, Russia, India, France, Peru, Egypt
Wheat	North Europe, India, Russia, Italy, Australia
Cotton	Mexico, Bahama Islands, Egypt
Tobacco	South America, West Indies
Sorghum	Egypt, Sudan, Natal, South Africa
Potatoes	Europe
Oranges	Azores, Brazil, *in situ*
Rice	Honduras, Japan, Philippines, Madagascar
Tomatoes	England, France, *in situ*
Peanuts	Spain, Brazil
Oats	Mexico, Uruguay, Russia, Australia
Barley	Mexico, Scotland, Germany, Russia, Balkans, Turkey
Sugar Beet	Europe

Source: Dr. Jack Harlan. Unpublished manuscript.

North America's barley crop has had particular difficulty adapting to a new continent. Disease-resistance comes primarily from Algeria but present varieties also contain genetic material from Egypt, Russia and China. Powdery mildew resistance in barley traces to Manchuria while 'barley yellow dwarf' — a new disease — is only blocked by one gene introduction from Ethiopia. If 'barley yellow dwarf' became a major problem, the entire world crop would be dependent upon this single Ethiopian gene.[30]

*　　　　*　　　　*

When you settle down to dinner tonight, there will be nothing on your plate that does not come to you directly, and/or indirectly, from the Third World. Our food system is vastly more interdependent than most of us would have imagined. Should anything happen to severely reduce the genetic diversity of the Third World, or make it impossible for the First World to obtain vital germ plasm, the potential for a world-wide food crisis would be very real. It is apparent that the 'gene-poor' nations outside the Vavilov Centres must continue to look to the Third World for genetic support.

REFERENCES

1. *The National Program for the Conservation of Crop Germ Plasm.* US Department of Agriculture, June 1971, p. 9.

2. Wilkes, G., "The Endangered Genetic Base of the World's Food Supply", *The Bulletin of the Atomic Scientist.* February 1977, p. 11.

3. Myers, N., "Disappearing Legacy: The Earth's Vanishing Genetic Heritage", *Nature Canada.* October/December 1978, p. 44.

4. Kendrick Jr., J. B., "Preserving our Genetic Resources", *California Agriculture.* September 1977, p. 2.

5. Omang, J., "Plants with Alien Names Hold Promise of a Brave New World", *The Washington Post.* September 28, 1978.

6. Grubben, G. J. H., *Tropical Vegetables and their Genetic Resources.* IBPGR, 1977, p. 7.

7. Eckholm, E., *Disappearing Species: The Social Challenge.* July 1978.

8. Kendrick Jr., J. B., op. cit., p. 2.

9. Wilkes, G., "Native Crops and Wild Food Plants", *Ecologist.* Vol. 7 No. 8, p. 313.

10. Oldfield. M. L., *The Utilization and Conservation of Genetic Resources: An Economic Analysis.* Master of Science Thesis, March 1977, p. 63.

11. Wilkes, G., op. cit., p. 313.

12. Fogg, H. G. W., *History of Popular Garden Plants from A to Z.* 1976, p. 1.

13. Perelman, M., *Farming for Profit in a Hungry World.* Landmark Series, 1977, p. 144.

14. Harlan, J. R., "Gene Centres and Gene Utilization". Unpublished Manuscript.

15. *Handbook of Canadian Varieties of Barley, Field Beans, Field Peas, Flax, Oats, Rye, and Spring, Durum and Winter Wheat.* Agriculture Canada, 1975.

16. *The National Program for the Conservation of Crop Germ Plasm.* US Department of Agriculture, June 1971, p. 9.

17. Ibid., p. 47.

18. Ibid., p. 47.

19. Ibid., p. 46.

20. Ibid., p. 52.

21. Ibid., p. 56.

22. Harlan, J. R., op. cit..

23. *The National Program for the Conservation of Crop Germ Plasm.* US Department of Agriculture, June 1971, pp. 56-7.

24. Ibid., p. 43.

25. Ibid., p. 60.

26. Eckholm, E., op. cit., p. 12.

27. *The National Program for the Conservation of Crop Germ Plasm.* US Department of Agriculture, June 1971, p. 40.

28. Ibid., p. 42.

29. Martens, J. W., Taken from a speech made at the "Chemicals in Agriculture" Conference in Saskatchewan, Canada, 1977.

30. Schaller, C. W., "Utilizing Genetic Diversity on the Improvement of Barley Cultivars", *California Agriculture.* September 1977, pp. 18-19.

Chapter 2

Genetic Erosion

Suddenly in the 1970s, we are discovering Mexican farmers growing hybrid corn seed from a midwestern seed firm, Tibetan farmers planting barley from a Scandinavian plant breeding station, and Turkish farmers planting wheat from the Mexican programme. Each of these classic areas of crop-specific genetic diversity is rapidly becoming an area of seed uniformity.
— Dr. Garrison Wilkes, Boston, Mass., USA, 1977.

The process represents a paradox in social and economic development in that the product of technology (breeding for yield and uniformity) displaces the resource upon which the technology is based.
— US National Academy of Sciences, 1978.

2.1 The 'Erosion' Process

As the previous chapter mentioned, the genetic diversity of the Third World has been greatly diminished. The ongoing destruction of the Vavilov Centres will ultimately lead to increased genetic uniformity and vulnerability for the world's crops. Dr. J.G. Hawkes of the University of Birmingham has referred to centuries of genetic material being 'swept away'[1]; Dr. Jack Harlan has called the process genetic 'wipe-out'.[2] More sedate in its terminology, the FAO has spoken of 'erosion'.[3] Warnings have been sounded about this situation since at least World War II, yet no one listened until blight suddenly struck the US corn crop in 1970, leaving the southern states with only half a harvest. Suddenly, the First World's genetic poverty became apparent to all. Dr. William Caldwell of the USDA commented: "We were sitting around fat, dumb and happy . . . the hybrids were doing well and all of a sudden the disease hit. We didn't believe it could happen, but it did."[4] A disease first reported in the Philippines eight years earlier had suddenly attacked the Texas (T) Cytoplasm, common to almost all hybrids growing in the South.[5] The proliferation of brand name maize varieties had disguised the fundamental genetic uniformity of corporate seed corn development. Frustrated and angry farmers have had several companies in the law courts battling class action suits ever since.[6]

Plant genetic diversity is forever being created and destroyed. It should alarm no one that some genetic material which might ultimately have been of use to major crops has been, and is, vanishing. What should cause concern is the massive, wholesale eradication of irreplaceable breeding material over thousands of square miles of arable land. This is what genetic 'erosion' refers to. Biologist Thomas Lovejoy estimates a loss of one-sixth of the world's living species by the end of this century.[7] Fellow biologist George M. Woodwell describes genetic 'erosion' as: "One of the great issues of our time... right up there with nuclear proliferation... the ultimate resource is the biota — there is no other. And we are destroying it."[8] The Director of the Missouri Botanical Gardens, Peter Raven, calculates that every disappearing plant variety takes with it from ten to thirty other plant or animal species dependent upon it for survival.[9] The 'endangered species' list now accounts for ten percent of the plant life indigenous to North America; and the situation is no less critical in Europe.[10]

Genetic 'erosion' means far more than a theoretical loss for future scientists: "Quite literally, the genetic diversity of a millennium in a particular variety can disappear in a single bowl of porridge."[11] This is what happened to uncounted varieties of wheat in Afghanistan, when food aid encouraged farmers to eat their old seed.[12] Dr. Erna Bennett of the FAO's Crop Ecology Unit tells another story of wheat in Greece, where new high-yielding varieties in the valleys drove traditional hillside farmers out of the market. Invaluable breeding material — important to the Australasian islands, Argentina, France and North America — simply vanished.[13] In an interview in *Ceres* a few years ago, Dr. Jack Harlan spoke of his own experience in Turkey where he encountered virtually thousands of flax varieties growing on the Cilician plain. When he returned 20 years later only one variety remained — and this was imported from Argentina.[14]

2.2 The Lessons of History

The genetic uniformity of a crop amounts to an invitation for an epidemic to destroy that crop. The uniformity itself may result from the inherent pressures of the market place (machine harvesting, processing, etc.), as well as the absence of genetic variety in the crop breeding programme. As 'erosion' spreads in the Vavilov Centres, the danger of crop epidemics in the industrialized world will increase. Southern corn leaf blight is only the most recent of a long history of epidemics common to every continent.

Historically, the most dramatic example in the western world was the Irish Potato Famine of the late 1840s. At a European symposium on plant breeding held in the summer of '78, Dr. J. G. Hawkes traced the disastrous potato blight back to its root causes in South America.[15] English explorers returned from the Caribbean coast in the 16th century with only one variety of potato. Planted everywhere in northern Europe, it was only a matter of time until this genetically-uniform crop was struck by blight. In a remarkably short space of time, the Irish lost their primary food source, leaving at least two million dead and two million more searching for a new life in other countries.[16] Although significant efforts have since been made to diversify potato varieties, Europe still remains vulnerable and in need of additional genetic material.

Coffee rust has destroyed crops in Sri Lanka, India, Java, Malaysia, the Philippines and a dozen African countries. In fact, epidemics are particularly common to the plantation crops of the Third World, where the crops are grown for export by Western companies: 'Panama banana disease' was prevalent throughout the West Indies at the turn of the century; 'mosaic virus' struck sugar cane in the 1920s, devastating the Louisiana crop in 1926 until relief was found with introductions of wild sugar cane from Java; 'witches bloom' destroyed cacao crops until new, wild material could be bred; and, 'mosaic virus' struck tobacco estates repeatedly until some immunity was found in Colombia.[17]

However, internal 'erosion' not only affects the Third World's export crops. Writing in the *Ecologist* in 1974, P. John described the impact of highly-uniform, high-yielding maize hybrids in Zambia. Commercial farmers in that country usually provide about 90% of domestic needs. In 1974, a new mold attacked the maize crop; 20% of the hybrids were infested, but the impact upon traditional maize varieties grown by villagers was negligible.[18] A year after southern corn leaf blight struck the United States, a vastly more devastating 'wipe-out' took India's 'pearl millet' crop. Once again, the 'pearl millet' was a highly-uniform but high-yielding hybrid. When male sterile cytoplasm was attacked by a form of downy mildew it was defenceless; and since 1971, the epidemic has struck parts of the millet crop each year. Recounting the tragedy at a 1977 symposium, Dr. K. M. Safeeulla of Mysore said that while the US corn blight "triggered a chain reaction that ultimately led to an upward movement of prices", the 'pearl millet' wipe-out in India "led to starvation, imports of food grains and a depletion of foreign exchange."[19]

In the West, the best known disaster is 'Dutch elm disease'. North Americans know the disease by that name because US veneer companies imported the diseased trees from France and Holland.[20] The genetic vulnerability of grapes generates equal concern in some Europeans and North Americans. For example, the French have been experiencing successive epidemics in their vineyards for the past one hundred and fifty years. Uniformity has been the culprit.[21]

Wheat has had an especially long legacy of vulnerability. The Roman God, Robigus, was summoned out of mythology as far back as 700 B.C., to protect Italian wheat fields from rust. Rust in wheat has devastated French fields for centuries and can be expected to create famine conditions at least once a decade. In North America, stem rust destroyed two million bushels of US wheat and a million bushels of Canadian wheat in 1916; this led to the call for two 'wheatless' days a week in 1917.[22] 'Ceres' wheat was developed in Dakota in 1926, to fend off rust in hard red spring wheat. By 1934, 'Ceres' occupied 35% of US spring wheat acreage. In 1935, a rust mutation destroyed the crop.[23] Wheat stem rust returned to the USA and Canada in 1953, to eliminate 65% of the durum wheat crop. In some parts of North America, up to 75% of the durum crop vanished in the early and mid-seventies, along with about 25% of the bread wheat.[24] Michael Allaby wrote: "Overnight, extreme resistance had been replaced by extreme vulnerability."[25] Stripe rust struck the Sacramento Valley in 1974, causing up to 100% crop loss in spring wheat. The CIMMYT — International Maize and Wheat Improvement Centre — in Mexico has become a major source of breeding material for Californian farmers fighting rust.[26] Today, both Canada and the United States grow 'Pitic' wheat varieties first developed in Mexico.

2.3 Ongoing Lessons

As a result of the corn blight, the US National Academy of Sciences (NAS) produced two studies. In 1972, *Genetic Vulnerability of Major Crops* — a report prepared by a committee under the chairmanship of Dr. James D. Horsfell — was released.[27] The report concluded that US crops are "impressively uniform genetically and impressively vulnerable." The committee also noted: "This uniformity derives from powerful economic and legislative forces."[28] The vulnerability of certain US crops, as well as Canada's grain crops, is well illustrated in Table 3; and apparently, similar figures could be produced for Australia:

Table 3
Crop Genetic Vulnerability

CANADA		
CROP	**VARIETIES**	%
Bread Wheat	4	75.9
Flax	4	92.3
Rapeseed	4	95.8
Oats	4	65.1
Barley	3	63.7
Rye	4	80.5
USA		
CROP	**VARIETIES**	%
Millet	3	100
Cotton	3	53
Soybeans	6	56
Dry Beans	2	60
Snap Beans	3	76
Peas	2	96
Corn	6	71
Potatoes	4	72
Sweet Potatoes	1	69

Sources: *The Prairie Pools: Crop Acreage Report,* 1978.
US National Academy of Sciences, 1972.

In 1978, the Academy released a second report, *Conservation of Germ Plasm Resources: An Imperative*. The committee responsible once again launched a powerful attack, warning the scientific community about the dangers of 'erosion' and reaffirming the findings of the earlier report. Contacted a year after the report was published, the Chairman, Dr. Elizabeth Russell, was guardedly optimistic about the situation[29]; whereas Dr. Horsfell reported "no discernible change", when his comments were sought in early 1979.[30]

In fact, the situation is undoubtedly worse with regards to export crops so central to the economies of Third World nations. Michael Allaby writes that the East Malling Research Station and the Wye College (London University) are actively cloning coconut trees to speed up their multiplication. In the near future, coconut estates in Asia may all contain genetically identical trees, which will make them highly susceptible to disease.[31] Similar work is being done with oil palms in an attempt to produce shorter and faster growing trees.[32] In their 1977 annual reports, Goodyear and Firestone Tire Companies both emphasized the wide-scale planting of new high-yielding rubber trees in plantations spread from Brazil to Indonesia. Multinational firms, who own and market these crops, can benefit substantially as long as they maintain several sources of supply — e.g. coconut estates in Malaysia, Indonesia and Sri Lanka; because an epidemic in one country will not necessarily affect the harvest in another. However, this type of plant breeding does not usually benefit the Third World countries involved.

What events have come together in the final quarter of the twentieth century to cause the destruction of the Vavilov Centres? Responding to our request for information, Dr. C. Dorsman of the Wageningen Gene Bank in Holland laid the blame at the feet of urbanization, tree-cutting, overgrazing and the introduction of new high-yielding Green Revolution varieties.[33] For example, wheat — the world's foremost cereal — appears to be uniquely and urgently endangered.[34] Wheat erosion occurred at such a rate in the Near East under the advance of the Green Revolution (i.e. between the mid-sixties and mid-seventies), that Dr. Bennett and others at the FAO anticipate the complete loss of the Near East 'centre' by the end of the eighties.[35] Such a loss could have terrible implications for world wheat crops by early in the next century.

2.4   Wild Species

The world's farmers might be somewhat comforted if it were known which of the world's plant species were being eliminated, but unfortunately this is not the case. To compound the problem, the world is losing hundreds of thousands of wild species, some of which are close relatives of cultivated varieties. Their loss could have a direct impact on the viability of future food resources.

In highland Guatemala, forester Thomas Veblan reported, one of the world's few tropical coniferous forests is on the verge of disappearing before its economic potential can even be studied. In a 1976 study, Adrien Somer

Table 4
Commonly Used Pharmaceutical Plants

PLANT/DRUG	SOURCE	PURPOSE
Ipecac root	Brazil	Amoebic Dysentry
		Induce Vomiting
Myrrh	Ethiopia	Astringent
		Irritation-healing Mouthwash
Colchicum Seed	Italy	Gout
Autumn Crocus		Gout
Peru Balsam	El Salvador	Sooths skin ulcers and
		hemorrhoids
Rhubarb roots	India	Laxative
Psyllium seeds		Laxative
Aloe	Caribbean	Pain-reliever
Cascara Sagrada	USA	Laxative
Senna Leaves	Egypt	Laxative
Ground Pumpkin Seed	China	Worm-killer
		Snail-fever
Mayapple	USA	Attacks Cancer
Madagascar Periwinkle	India	Hodgkin's Disease
		Childhood Leukemia
Rauwolfa root	India	Tranquilizer
	Africa	High Blood Pressure
Coca Bush	South America	Eases pain
Curare	South America	Muscle relaxant in surgery
Ouabain	Africa	Stimulant for cardiac cases
Calabar Beans	West Africa	Attacks Glaucoma
Castor Bushes	Egypt	Castor Oil
Velvet Bean Vines	Egypt	Parkinson's Disease
Purple Foxglove	UK	Digitalis-Heart stimulant
Faskorn	Nigeria	Stomach complaints
Nightshade	Middle East	Eye relaxant
Henbane	Middle East	Eye relaxant
Mandrake	Middle East	Eye relaxant
Thornapple	Middle East	Eye relaxant
Green-Stemmed Shrub	China	Asthma
Ephedrine	China	Hay Fever
		Low Blood Pressure
Cinchona	Andes	Malaria cure

Source: Aikman, L., "Nature's Gifts to Medicine", *National Geographic*, September 1974.

concluded that a forest area the size of Cuba is destroyed every year and that 40% of the world's tropical moist forests have already been eliminated.[36] Ruthless logging operations — often conducted by major corporations — have been singled out by some FAO officials as a major cause of this. In a tough 1975 talk to the American Paper Institute, the Assistant Director-General of the FAO, Dr. K. F. S. King, spoke of the righteous anger of Third World countries towards the logging industry: "...they have seen huge dividends declared by some operating in their countries and have failed to observe any comparable development of their peoples; they have noticed that a few foreign operators have ruthlessly devastated and raped their forests and other natural resources and have left the countries, after they have done this, poorer than when they came. They have not manufactured these charges. There are examples in almost every developing country."[37] Mindful that ancient Babylon fell, not through war, but by cutting down its trees, forest-rich nations like Malaysia, Indonesia and Brazil are beginning to reconsider their 'supposedly' renewable resources.[38]

The world looks not only to wild species for food and shelter but also for modern medicines. A 1967 US study revealed that fully 25% of all prescription drugs sold on the American market are derived directly from plant material. This amounts to US $3 billion annually. A follow-up survey, conducted in 1978, suggested this percentage cannot be expected to diminish in this century.[39] Including microbes and animals, over 40% of US prescription drugs are derived from nature.[40] One report noted: "The humblest bacterium can synthesize in the course of its brief existence more organic compounds than can all the world's chemists combined."[41] To the surprise of many, modern medicine remains heavily dependent upon plant material.

Dependence upon plants means dependence upon the Third World. Alkaloid-bearing plants are twice as prevalent in the tropics as in temperate zones. Alkaloids, of vital importance to medicine, have been studied in only 40% of known plants. Tanzania provides over 500 plants, currently used in Chinese medicine, that are largely untested in the West. Recognizing that medically useful plants were especially endangered in the Philippines, international agencies began work in the summer of 1978 to collect over 1,000 medically beneficial plants. The importance of this work might be summed up by considering the poke weed. This plant's chemical make-up appears to offer the world a solution to bilharzia (snail fever) — a disease currently affecting the health of over 200 million people in the Third World.[42]

*   *   *

The Green Revolution vastly increased the productive capacity of some major crops. However, genetic conservation should also have been incorporated in the various crop development schemes, since the genetic wealth of an area can simply vanish within a few years under the production pressure of a single imported variety. Before examining some of the legislative and corporate causes of 'erosion', we will look at the work presently underway which is attempting to ameliorate the disappearance of plant germ plasm.

REFERENCES

1. Eckholm, E., *Disappearing Species: The Social Challenge*. July 1978, p. 13.
2. "The Green Revolution: Genetic Backlash", *Ceres — The FAO Review*. September-October 1969.
3. From a telephone conversation with E. Bennett on June 28, 1978.
4. Jones, R.A., "Food Peril: Erosion of Wild Plants". Article is from an unknown newspaper.
5. Allaby, M., "Miracle Rice Breeds Miracle Locusts", *Ecologist.* p. 181.
6. Firms involved include Anderson Clayton, Dekalb and Pioneer Hi-Bred.
7. Eckholm, E., op. cit., p. 7.
8. Ibid., p. 18.
9. Ibid., p. 6.
10. Ibid., p. 6.
11. Wilkes, G., "The Endangered Genetic Base of the World's Food Supply", *The Bulletin of the Atomic Scientist.* February 1977, p. 11.
12. Frankel, O.H., *Survey of Crop Genetic Resources in their Centres of Diversity*. FAO, 1973, p. 22.
13. From a telephone conversation with E. Bennett on June 26, 1978.
14. "The Green Revolution: Genetic Backlash", *Ceres — The FAO Review*. September-October 1969.
15. The symposium was held in the Netherlands in July, 1978.
16. Woodham-Smith, C., *The Great Hunger*. Harper & Row, 1962.
17. Harlan, J. R., "Genetic Resources in Wild Relatives of Plants", *Crop Science*. May-June 1976, p. 329.
18. John, P., "The Green Revolution Turns Sour", *Ecologist*. 1974, pp. 304-5.
19. Safeeulla, K.M., "Genetic Vulnerability: The Basis of Recent Epidemics in Agriculture", in Day, P.R. ed., *The Genetic Basis of Epidemics in Agriculture*. New York Academy of Sciences, 1977, p. 78.
20. *Genetic Vulnerability of Major Crops*. US National Academy of Sciences, 1972, p. 19.
21. Ibid., p. 18.
22. Ibid., p. 18.
23. "The Green Revolution: Genetic Backlash", *Ceres — The FAO Review*. September-October 1969.
24. Wilkes, G., op. cit., p. 15.
25. Allaby, M., op. cit., p. 181.
26. Qualset, C.O. et al., "Breeding Successes with Spring Wheat Germ Plasm", *California Agriculture*. September 1977, p. 27.
27. *Genetic Vulnerability of Major Crops*. US National Academy of Sciences, 1972.
28. Ibid., p. 1.
29. From a telephone interview with Dr. Russell in March, 1979.
30. From a telephone interview with Dr. Horsfell in March, 1979.
31. Allaby, M., op. cit., p. 181.
32. Harlan, J.R., op. cit., p. 330.
33. From personal correspondence dated October 24, 1978.

34. *Priorities Among Crops and Regions.* CGIAR, 1976, p. 6.

35. From a telephone conversation with E. Bennett on June 26, 1978.

36. Eckholm, E., op. cit., p. 10.

37. Aggrwala, N., "World's Forest Resources". UNDP/FAO, 1975.

38. Eckholm, E., op. cit., p. 36.

39. *Conservation of Germ Plasm Resources: An Imperative.* US National Academy of Sciences, 1978, p. 33.

40. Eckholm, E., op. cit., p. 21.

41. Ibid., p. 17.

42. Ibid., pp. 17-18.

Chapter 3

Genetic Conservation

It would be nice to think that all the genetic diversity we will ever need is safely stored away in gene banks for future use. Unfortunately, this is hardly the case. The National Seed Storage Laboratory has received stepchild treatment with no increase in its operating budget for more than 15 years after establishment.
— Dr. Jack Harlan, University of Illinois, USA, 1975.

We have met with constant difficulties because of a marked lack of financial support. The financial resources that we require are of an order that is infinitesimally small compared with sums that mankind devotes to far less constructive purposes.
— Sir Otto Frankel, Canberra, Australia, 1969.

Our governments, both provincial and federal, have so far shown no appreciable concern, not to speak of encouragement and financial support for research in the area of sampling techniques, collection, conservation and management of plant genetic resources.
— Dr. S. Jana, University of Saskatchewan, Canada, 1979.

3.1   The Conservation 'Network'

Superficially, the world's genetic resources appear to be protected by a formidable international network of gene banks, crop research centres, super seed laboratories and research dollars. Central to this network is the IBPGR — the International Board for Plant Genetic Resources. Based in Rome, the board attempts to co-ordinate the regional work undertaken by eight international crop research stations, strategically located in the prime Vavilov Centres. There are also approximately sixty nationally-controlled gene banks, whose work the IBPGR has to consider.[1] The IBPGR, the stations and the banks are all supported by the National Seed Storage Laboratory (NSSL) in the USA. The NSSL rates special status according to the IBPGR, since it "maintains material as a base collection for the United States and for the global network of genetic resource centres."[2] Its global collections include maize, sorghum, wheat and rice. Comparable to the NSSL is the N.I. Vavilov Gene Bank in the USSR — a centre which probably contains a more diversified collection of wild and cultivated material.[3]

The dollars involved in global agriculture might also seem substantial at first glance. In preparation for the 1974 World Food Conference, the FAO reported that total agricultural research for all countries amounted to US $1,560 million.[4] However, 85% of this is spent within the western world; little of which goes to basic collection and conservation programmes.[5] It is because government policies and budgets pose real restrictions, that the IBPGR only presumes to speak of an 'emerging' conservation network.[6]

The International Board for Plant Genetic Resources

The genetic fate of the world may well rest upon the courageous but narrow shoulders of the International Board for Plant Genetic Resources. With a secretariat of six and a budget of well under US $3 million in 1979, the IBPGR owes its existence to the CGIAR (Consultative Group on International Agricultural Research); a group whose 34 member governments, plus the Rockefeller, Ford and Kellogg Foundations, operate under the benevolent eyes of the World Bank and the UN Development Programme (UNDP).[7]

The IBPGR's primary task is to create an international network. En route, the board is creating: an international information data bank, known as IS/GR (Information Sciences/Genetic Resources Programme); a training programme; a conservation programme, i.e. support for storage facilities and basic research into conservation; and, special initiatives related to the conservation of special crops and regional conservation programmes. A great deal of the work focuses on the Vavilov Centres of genetic diversity, and on exploration and storage programmes related to these centres. Via a host of advisory bodies, the IBPGR has also established a priority collection system for endangered seed varieties. As a point of interest, wheat heads the list.[8]

The IBPGR is an independent body with its members elected as individuals, not as representatives. Geographically, there are three from North America; six from Europe; and, five from the Third World — plus two ex-officio members representing the FAO and UN Environment Programme (UNEP). The board meets twice annually, while its Executive Committee gathers four times a year. The board has two major advisory committees: one is related to the information function; and the other is concerned with specific crops.[9] Corporate representation is provided by Dr. W. I. Brown (President of Pioneer Hi-Bred International), who chairs the key Crop Germ Plasm Advisory Committee; and Dr. L. N. Branscomb (Vice-President and Chief Scientist at IBM), who sits on the Advisory Committee on the Genetic Resources Communications, Information and Documentation System (GR/CIDS).[10] Heavy reliance is also placed on the Crop Ecology and Genetic Resources Service of the FAO Plant Production and Protection Division.

The IBPGR got underway in 1974 with an especially modest budget of US $570,000 and was still operating at under a million dollars in 1976. Given its role as co-ordinator, the board does not anticipate large sums for itself and assumes a peak annual figure of about US $3 million by 1981.[11] Donors include ten large sources — nine governments and the UNEP. Of the nine governments, six are European and the remainder are the USA, Saudi Arabia and Canada. Total grants in 1977 amounted to US $932,654 of which 65.8% (US $613,791) went to industrialized nations. The lion's share went to the USA (US $416,050), to support the documentation programme at the NSSL. Since the USA only contributed US $200,000 in 1977, it made a net profit on the year.[12]

Table 5
IBPGR's 1977 Donors

DONOR	CURRENCY	CONTRIBUTION
Belgium	B.F.	2,000,000
Canada	Can. $	95,000
Fed. Rep. of Germany	D.M.	100,000
Netherlands	US $	100,000
Norway	N. Kr.	500,000
Saudi Arabia	US $	10,000
Sweden	S Kr.	1,400,000
United Kingdom	£ Stg.	45,000
UNEP	US $	100,000
United States	US $	200,000

Source: IBPGR 1977 Annual Report.

The National Seed Storage Laboratory

Closely connected to the IBPGR is the National Seed Storage Laboratory at Fort Collins, Colorado — the world's storehouse for many major crops. The NSSL opened its doors in September 1958, with a budget of US $450,000.[13] No increase in its operating budget was received until the mid-seventies; and the laboratory is still insufficiently funded.[14] The entire facility, constructed above ground, now stands equidistant between one of the largest munitions manufacturing plants in the USA and a nuclear reactor.[15] Aside from this unfortunate oversight, how is the world's central bank for plant genes protected? The doors are locked at night, and the Colorado State University campus police keep a watch on the building. One staffer described the laboratory as "a sitting duck" and stressed "zero bomb or radiation protection."[16]

If something less than the Fort Knox of plants, the laboratory is still greatly prized by major seed companies who "show the most active interest and concern."[17] They should, since 25% of the world gene bank's storage space is devoted to 'ornamental type material' with a high profit potential. In October 1978, the Director of the laboratory, Dr. Louis N. Baas wrote: "I don't believe any government has provided sufficient funds to do the entire task." He went on to say: "The need for a crash programme is quite great in some kinds of seeds. For example, the situation that happened with the wheat varieties."[18] Baas scores high marks in the international community for his personal concern about genetic 'erosion' and his own efforts to 'get things moving'.

23

Map 2

Major International Crop Research Stations

Source: IBPGR 1977 Annual Report.

The International Crop Research Stations

Sharing the IBPGR's tie to the World Bank and CGIAR, the eight international crop research stations have been perceived as playing a key role in the collecting and cataloguing of material found in the Vavilov Centres. Important though this role may be, the stations have inadvertently contributed to the prevailing myth that conservation programmes are well developed. For years, plant breeders in New Zealand, France and elsewhere have gone about their work assuming that great things were being done at these centres; whereas in fact, difficulties already existed in fulfilling their primary commitment, which was to develop new crop varieties. By and large, collection programmes have tended to be very specific, with emphasis on yield and uniformity characteristics. Harlan noted: "Most of our so-called world collections are sadly deficient in wild races . . . This should be remedied soon or it will be too late in many crops."[19] This view is shared by the US National Academy of Sciences, whose 1978 study deplored "the tendency of many important issues to fall between the cracks of existing commitments such that no one takes responsibility for facing up to them."[20]

In part, the gaps arise with single-crop stations operating in centres of multi-crop diversity. Vegetable and other subsistent crops, excluding the major grains, tend to be low in priority. However, even the major crops need more collecting. In Indonesia, for example, Dr. S. Sastraradja recently told the IBPGR that several economically important land races of rice and sorghum had not been collected in his country, and were in danger of disappearing.[21] One of the more notable losses was the carving wood used in Bali — exhausted by the demands of the tourist trade.[22]

In a 1973 survey for the FAO, leading experts catalogued a dismaying array of collection needs.[23] Dr. E. Kjelluviet singled out the loss of einkorn wheat in Turkey.[24] Reviewing wheat in the Mediterranean zone, Erna Bennett commented that all cereals "are in a highly precarious position."[25] In Iraq, local varieties have been replaced by imports from Mexico.[26] The 'cereals' situation in Syria was termed serious.[27] Kjelluviet viewed the barley scene in Turkey as most urgent and admitted that while the oat situation was not so severe in that country, plant breeders in Canada and Scandinavia were anxious for further collections.[28] Further corn collections were also urgently required in Spain where commercial hybrids were replacing traditional material.[29] More corn collecting was needed in Mexico and Guatemala, even though the CIMMYT had been operating in Mexico since World War II.[30]

National Gene Banks

At the bottom of the genetic conservation ladder are the sixty or so national gene banks, formed to collect and preserve national treasures and to gather from the world's resources whatever material may be required by local plant breeders. For several years now, the UNDP and FAO have worked unsuccessfully with the curators of European gene banks to build a continent-wide conservation strategy. Many countries, including Canada, believe that

Map 3
Major Gene Banks

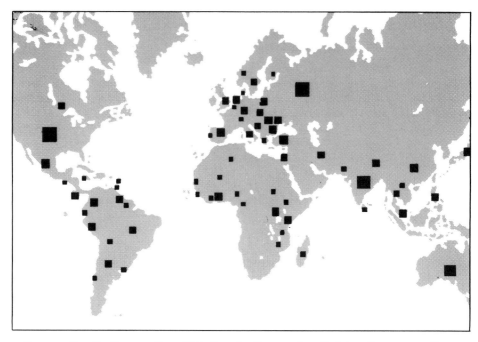

Source: *Genetic Conservation.* FAO Genetic Conservation Training Programme, Crop Ecology and Genetic Resources Unit, FAO, PI/F7460.

the Americans have a master system. Since the collection system became official in 1898, the US government has supported well over 150 overseas expeditions which have brought home over 350,000 new plants.[31] A 1978 report on the 'National Plant Germ Plasm System' identified eleven major gene banks with a total of 276,124 plant introductions.[32] Like the IBPGR, the Americans speak of a system which tends to look a good deal better on maps and charts than it does in dollars and cents. At five to seven overseas expeditions a year, the USA is running far behind its own identified needs.[33] Dr. Desmond Dolan of the Geneva, New York gene bank privately estimates a total federal collections budget of not more than US $35,000-$40,000 per annum.[34]

The National Plant Genetic Resources Board met in Washington in mid-May of 1978, after being suspended by the Carter Administration from July 1977 to February 1978.[35] Board members took heart that the policy review ultimately brought them back into existence. Dr. Charles Adamson of the Savannah, Georgia gene bank spoke of increased recognition within the USDA, but countered: ". . . the agency itself has declined. I think that government efforts in this area will always suffer from an unwillingness to admit the inability to set priorities."[36] It would, therefore, seem unwise for other countries to look solely to the USA to conserve the world's genetic resources.

In comparison to its northern neighbour, however, the American system shines. Committed through the IBPGR to safeguard the world's barley resources, Canada's Expert Committee on Plant Genetic Resources met in November 1977 to review its programme. Urgent discussion centered upon the need for a new storage unit at the Ottawa Research Station, to support new accesssions from abroad as well as local resources. The committee noted that it had struggled for three years to persuade higher levels within Agriculture Canada to provide the required funding. In some despair, committee members proposed approaches to the Canadian International Development Agency (CIDA) or the International Development Research Centre (IDRC). An approach to IBPGR was also suggested until it was pointed out that a request for C $25,000 might prove embarrassing.[37] By October 1978, however, Dr. Roland Loiselle of the Ottawa gene bank was able to report that officials were prepared to provide the additional storage unit, as well as support a conservation programme: "... although no immediate action is contemplated because of budgetary restraints."[38]

Canada's national programme appears to operate on about C $60,000 a year with a core staff of one and a half people in Ottawa.[39] Beyond Ottawa, there are 36 other gene banks in Canada, ranging from proper storage units to kitchen-style freezers. Most are at the level of very small working collections.[40] Despite the best efforts of Loiselle and his committee, fewer than a third of those possessing working collections were responding to requests for data from Agriculture Canada by the time he reported to the committee in late 1977.[41] It is clear that no one in Canada knows what is being spent, or by whom, on genetic conservation; or what is on hand in storage. As for expeditions abroad, one telephone request for information to Ottawa

Map 4
US National Plant Germ Plasm System

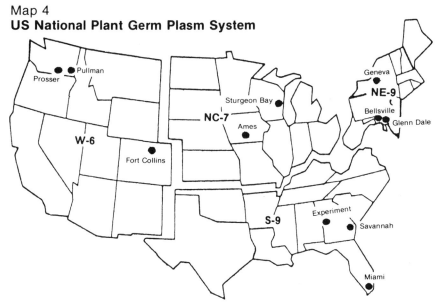

Source: USDA, 1977.

27

committee chairman, Dr. Charles Bishop, resulted in a plea for funds to finance excursions to the Near East.[42] In criticizing the poor response to requests for data by Canadian plant breeders, Dr. Loiselle has noted: "This attitude . . . is not that much different from that at the executive level within Agriculture Canada where the subject of gene resources receives only token support in terms of funding."[43] However, in response to political pressure, Agriculture Canada officials have recently begun to talk about doing more for genetic conservation.[44]

If Western Europe and North America are neglecting their own needs, what are the centrally-planned governments doing? Conservation work in the Soviet Union, as we have already noted, got off to an early start. Sir Otto Frankel reports that the Russians continue to have the world's most representative collections.[45] In Yugoslavia, a new gene bank at Belgrade has gathered over 100,000 combinations of maize.[46] Czechoslovakian collections are also relatively extensive.[47] Until a recent US National Academy of Sciences study, the West was confident that conservation efforts in China were largely unnecessary due to the general practice among farmers of preserving their traditional seed. It now appears that many of the land races in wheat have been lost.[48] This is particularly sad news for Canadian and Scandinavian plant breeders. Scientific bodies in China are now moving to collect and store vanishing resources.[49]

Corporate Genes

It is also common knowledge that many large corporate concerns have substantial genetic collections of their own. The FAO reports that one company, United Brands (formerly United Fruit), has about two-thirds of the world's banana germ plasm in storage.[50] Staff at the major Canadian gene bank report that the private enterprise sector has failed to co-operate, by not divulging information on the quantity or type of genetic material it has in stock. Two companies have been specifically identified as having useful material which is not being shared in Canada: Maple Leaf Mills and Campbell Soup of Canada.[51] Many international researchers speculate that companies dominant in fruit and tree crops tend to pay close attention to their own genetic resource needs. The same may likewise be true for other export crops and companies.

For several years now, as invaluable collections — often controlled by concerned individuals and universities — have risked extinction, some major European firms have actively incorporated the germ plasm into their own genetic programmes. Since this material might otherwise have been lost, this kind of corporate involvement may be a blessing. However, Garrison Wilkes, bearing in mind a possible profit motive, strikes a cautionary note. After all, reduced genetic variability in any crop may increase dependence upon companies dominant in that crop.[52] M. L. Oldfield develops this analysis: "It follows, then, that any person or group who could successfully achieve private control over a variety of these genetic resources, whether they reside in a centralized cold storage facility or in a preserved environment, would indeed

28

possess almost infinite political and economic power."[53] Although little data is available, there is cause for concern. We need to know much more about the genetic stocks controlled by major companies, and we need to be assured that their material will be shared freely with other plant breeders and global governments.

3.2   Storehouse, Prison or Tomb?

It is folly to allow the idea to develop that it is okay to destroy habitats and retain all the species in zoos, botanical gardens or seed banks, with the dream of someday returning them to the wild.
— *The Co-Evolution Quarterly*, Fall 1978.

Not everyone in the scientific community is convinced that gene banks are the route to salvation for our disappearing plant species. Sharing some of this concern, in 1978 UNESCO declared 144 areas in 35 countries as future biosphere reserves.[54] Others in the scientific community view such resolutions and reserves as 'pie in the sky'. Roland Loiselle in Ottawa points out that proper gene bank storage can preserve wheat seeds for 390 years, and two-rowed barley for as long as 33,500 years.[55] Most plant breeders seem content with a system of gene banks and regular efforts to 'grow out' stored varieties. Generally, maize needs growing out every three years while the brassicas should be rejuvenated every four years.[56] The US National Academy of Sciences has noted the "failure to maintain" germ plasm collections in America over the past 35 years — particularly fruit, nut and vegetable collections.[57] According to the NAS: "After weighing all available measures for preserving endangered species under controlled conditions, we are repeatedly forced to the conclusion that the only reliable method is in the natural environment."[58]

Loss through storage, or through shipment to storage facilities, appears to be all too common. Forage crop collections in the Middle East and winged bean collections in Papua, New Guinea have narrowly escaped disaster in recent years. Canada's IDRC participated in a cassava collection expedition a few years back that resulted in the shipment loss of 500 Central American varieties.[59] Dr. Z. Huaman of Peru's CIP — International Potato Centre — alarmed the world's potato farmers by saying that despite numerous collections made during the fifty years prior to the establishment of the CIP, a large proportion of the collected cultivated material had been lost, leaving an inadequate sample of cultivated potato species in existing potato gene banks.[60] Huaman went on to say that the "indigenous reservoir...is threatened with extinction." In *Farming for Profit in a Hungry World*, author Michael Perelman reported: "...the failure of three refrigerator compressors resulting in the loss of a major Peruvian corn germ plasm collection. In addition, some irreplaceable corn collections were lost during the reorganization of a seed bank in Mexico."[61]

Gene banks are very vulnerable institutions. A power failure can raise storage temperatures or increase the humidity. Fires, floods and budget cuts place many collections in real jeopardy. Then there is the added problem that what is collected is often not well, or accurately, documented. To quote Sir Otto Frankel: "There is little known about the holdings of traditional cultivars in many of the larger collections... but they are neither large nor representative."[62] Important as gene banks may be, it would seem unwise for the world to put all its eggs in one basket.

The Third World, on the other hand, is being invited to put all its eggs in someone else's basket. The IBPGR 'ladder' might also be used to describe a flow of plant genetic material from the Vavilov Centres, to the international crop centres, to the NSSL in Colorado and the gene banks of the industrialized nations. Meanwhile, the original material is being destroyed when new, imported varieties are introduced by either the crop research stations or commercial enterprises overseas. The spread of crop uniformity and the removal of old material to gene banks — national or regional — effectively takes local farm families out of the plant breeding business. In this respect, the farmer's own government is left in a similar position, as invaluable national treasures disappear into the storage vaults of the NSSL or the N.I. Vavilov Centre in the USSR.

After a February 1979 visit to Kenya, the Development Press Service's Roy Laishley reported a conversation with Dr. W. Viertmann — an Australian with the FAO. Viertmann has been involved in a soil conservation scheme using Australian grasses and legumes to tie down the soil. Laishley said: "They are having to bring in tropical legumes seeds developed in Australia which were based on indigenous Kenya seeds." Therefore, at least a portion of Kenya's new grass and legume seeds has been commercially imported at some cost to the country. However, there was no record of Kenya receiving any payment for the raw material, shipped to Australia, which developed the new varieties.[63] Erna Bennett of the FAO reported an identical problem in Libya where forage seed, exported free to Australia, has been reimported in a slightly altered form at commercial prices.[64]

A FAO study concerning the sources of wheat collections held by the USDA demonstrates the absurdity of the Third World's position. By 1970, the USDA boasted material from 27 nations; only five were not in the Third World. American gene banks had stored more wheat varieties than were in identified collections in sixteen of the 27 countries. Fourteen countries — all Third World — had none of their own native wheat material in storage.[65] Put another way, as Afghanistan, Egypt and Korea watch the natural diversity of their agriculture become increasingly uniform, they will discover that virtually all of their rescued indigenous wheat varieties can only be obtained from the United States.

In fact, according to the US National Academy of Sciences, collection programmes are currently oriented to the needs of the developed countries.[66] US ratification of the International Convention on Trade in Endangered Species (May 23, 1977), may somewhat curb Third World losses. For example, more than 85 shipments containing over 8,000 plants have since been barred from US ports.[67] However, many Third World governments are no more worried about genetic losses than their industrialized counterparts; and those who are concerned lack the trained personnel and/or financial resources to act. Noting that "time is short", Dr. S. Sastrapradja of Indonesia has lately stressed the need for increased conservation programmes within the Third World.[68] The Association for the Advancement of Agricultural Sciences in Africa (AAASA) has called for an immediate survey of Africa's genetic resources; and wants to see acknowledgement of the conservation situation at national policy levels. According to the AAASA: "The crop genetic resources of every country are an invaluable national heritage. In the limited time that remains to gather them they must be preserved within and for each nation as well as for the world at large." Delegates at the 1978 AAASA gathering "strongly recommended" the formation of national programmes of action.[69] Sastrapradja agreed: "It is of prime importance that plant genetic resources be administered nationally."[70]

Gene banks are expensive propositions. The IBPGR roughly calculates that costs per accession range between a low of US $1.89 and a high of US $10.74.[71] To provide the Third World with a system of national gene banks and 'ecosphere reserves' could mean an initial outlay in excess of US $100 million, and annual costs of at least US $12 million. However, given the global importance of genetic resources, such an expenditure should be considered reasonable. Without their own gene banks, Third World governments may always have 'access', but they will never have 'control'.

Table 6
Seed Storage Costs

NUMBER OF ACCESSIONS SMALL TO LARGE STORAGE CAPACITY	US $ TOTAL COST	COST OF COLD ROOM & SHELVING PER ACCESSION	US $ TOTAL COST PER ACCESSION
22,800	$ 12,765-244,765	$ 1.20	$ 4.95-10.74
31,900	123,100-260,950	1.12	3.86-8.18
56,200	141,450-294,600	0.87	2.52-5.24
91,200	172,200-346,950	0.80	1.89-3.80

Source: *Report of IBPGR Working Group on Engineering, Design and Cost Aspects of Long-Term Seed Storage Facilities*, IBPGR, December 1976, pp. 6-7.

REFERENCES

1. Plant Genetic Resources of Canada (PGRC) Newsletter No. 5. October 1978, p. 5.

2. IBPGR Newsletter No. 36. January 1979, p. 8.

3. IBPGR Newsletter No. 33. February 1978, p. 33.

4. *The World Food Problem.* UN World Food Conference, November 1974, p. 96.

5. Ibid., p. 96.

6. IBPGR 1977 Annual Report p. 6.

7. "The Conservation of Crop Genetic Resources". IBPGR, 1975, p. 7.

8. IBPGR 1977 Annual Report.

9. Ibid., pp. 3-6.

10. Ibid., pp. 53-62.

11. From a June, 1978 telephone interview with J.L. Creech of the IBPGR (Board).

12. IBPGR 1977 Annual Report pp. 65-67.

13. *The National Program for the Conservation of Crop Germ Plasm.* US Department of Agriculture, June 1971, p. 22.

14. Harlan, J.R., "Our Vanishing Genetic Resources", *Science.* May 1975, p. 620.

15. From a telephone interview with Dr. Shane Smith in September, 1978.

16. From an interview conducted by Dr. Shane Smith with staff at Fort Collins in the fall of 1978. Reported to us in a telephone conversation in September, 1978.

17. Ibid..

18. From correspondence dated October 25, 1978.

19. Harlan, J.R., "Genetic Resources in Wild Relatives of Plants", *Crop Science.* May-June 1976.

20. *Conservation of Germ Plasm Resources: An Imperative.* US National Academy of Sciences, 1978, p. 3.

21. IBPGR Newsletter No. 34. June 1978, p. 10.

22. Ibid., p. 13.

23. Frankel, O.H. ed., *Survey of Crop Genetic Resources in their Centres of Diversity.* FAO, February 1973.

24. Ibid., p. 10.

25. Ibid., p. 1.

26. Ibid., p. 16.

27. Ibid., p. 15.

28. Ibid., p. 12.

29. IBPGR Newsletter No. 34. June 1978, p. 27.

30. *Conservation of Germ Plasm Resources: An Imperative.* US National Academy of Sciences, 1978, p. 97.

31. *The National Program for the Conservation of Crop Germ Plasm.* US Department of Agriculture, June 1971. Figures were drawn from various statistical tables.

32. *The National Plant Germ Plasm System.* USDA, Revised May 1978, p. 12.

33. *Conservation of Germ Plasm Resources: An Imperative.* US National Academy of Sciences, 1978, p. 28.

34. From a letter dated November 2, 1978.

35.　US National Plant Genetic Resources Board, May 18-19, 1978. Meeting minutes.

36.　From a letter dated November 1, 1978.

37.　Expert Committee on Plant Genetic Resources (Canada), November 24, 1977. Meeting minutes, p. 8.

38.　PGRC Newsletter No. 5. October 1978, p. 1.

39.　Provided by the Chief of the Seeds Division, Agriculture Canada in a January, 1978 telephone conversation. The information represents an informal estimate.

40.　Information provided from unpublished data by Dr. R. Loiselle of Agriculture Canada's Ottawa Research Station.

41.　Expert Committee on Plant Genetic Resources (Canada), November 24, 1977. Meeting minutes.

44.　Agriculture Canada convened a meeting of plant breeders in February, 1979, at which an extraordinary resolution was passed calling for 'someone' to do 'something' about genetic conservation as a priority issue.

45.　Frankel, O.H., "Genetic Conservation: Why and How". An undated speech made in Canberra, Australia.

46.　PGRC Newsletter No. 5. October 1978, p. 5.

47.　IBPGR Newsletter No. 36. January 1979, p. 25.

48.　IBPGR Newsletter No. 35. October 1978, p. 28.

49.　Ibid., p. 26.

50.　IBPGR Newsletter No. 33. February 1978, pp. 15-16.

51.　Information derived from a private conversation with Agriculture Canada sources.

52.　From an April 21, 1975 letter to F.M. Lappé from G. Wilkes.

53.　Oldfield, M.L., *The Utilization and Conservation of Genetic Resources: An Economic Analysis.* Master of Science Thesis, March 1977, p. 164.

54.　Eckholm, E., *Disappearing Species: The Social Challenge.* July 1978, p. 28.

55.　From a telephone conversation with Dr. R. Loiselle on June 1, 1978.

56.　Information summarized from a variety of generally available data sources.

57.　*Conservation of Germ Plasm Resources: An Imperative.* US National Academy of Sciences, 1978, p. 30.

58.　Ibid., p. 4.

59.　Kazuo Kawano, "Cassava Germ Plasm Collection and Advanced Genetic Material at CIAT", in *Cassava Germ Plasm.* IDRC conference report, 1975, p. 63.

60.　Huaman, Z., "Gene Bank Activities at the International Potato Centre". A speech made in July, 1978.

61.　Perelman, M., *Farming for Profit in a Hungry World.* Landmark Series, 1977, p. 156.

62.　Frankel, O.H., "Genetic Conservation: Why and How". An undated speech made in Canberra, Australia.

63.　From a letter from R. Laishley of the Development Press Service dated March 7, 1979.

64.　From a personal conversation with E. Bennett on March 20, 1979.

65.　*Genetic Vulnerability of Major Crops.* US National Academy of Sciences, 1972, p. 130.

66.　*Conservation of Germ Plasm Resources: An Imperative.* US National Academy of Sciences, 1978, p. 29.

67.　"Plant Importers Warned of Endangered Species Restrictions". USDA Regional Information Office (Chicago), August 25, 1978.

68.　IBPGR Newsletter No. 34. June 1978, p. 10.

69.   Ibid., p. 16.

70.   Ibid., p. 13.

71.   *Report of IBPGR Working Group on Engineering, Design and Cost Aspects of Long-Term Seed Storage Facilities.* IBPGR, December 1976, pp. 6-7.

The Seed Revolution

PHASE II OF THE GREEN REVOLUTION REVOLVES
AROUND THE SEED INDUSTRY...HOW IS THIS
PHASE DEVELOPING? WHO ARE THE NEW
SEEDSMEN? BY WHAT MEANS ARE THEY EVOLVING
A GLOBAL SEED INDUSTRY?

Chapter 4

The Green Revolution

A few years ago, one of the prized developments of the Green Revolution, a strain of rice known as IR-8, was hit by Tungro disease in the Philippines. When rice-growers switched to another form, IR-20, this hybrid soon proved badly vulnerable to grassy stunt virus and brown hopper insects. So farmers moved on to IR-26, a super-hybrid that turned out to be exceptionally resistant to almost all Philippine diseases and insect pests. But it proved too fragile to the islands' strong winds, whereupon plant breeders decided to try an original Taiwan strain that had shown an unusual capacity to stand up to winds — only to find that it had been all but eliminated by Taiwan farmers who by then had planted virtually all rice lands with IR-8.
— Dr. Norman Myers, Kenya, 1978.

The varieties produced by the Green Revolution did not produce as well as old known races; in many situations, because the seed supplies had been used for food, the people could not go back to their original strains. The fact resulted in food shortages in many areas.
— Dr. Norman Baas, National Seed Storage Laboratory, USA, 1978.

The Indonesian Government went much further ... It contracted with several international chemical companies who agreed to encourage farmers to adopt the new technology. In return, the government agreed to pay these firms $20 for every acre of land they succeeded in having planted to the new seeds. The results were disastrous. The programme was riddled with corruption. Needed farm inputs failed to arrive ... the insecticides killed the fish which provided a major portion of the protein for the people. Finally, a major famine occurred.
— Michael Perelman, *Farming for Profit in a Hungry World,* USA, 1977.

4.1 History and Scope

From its inception, the Green Revolution has been hotly debated by the scientific community and others. When Dr. Norman Borlaug picked up his Nobel Peace Prize in 1970, the Chairman of the Nobel Committee declared that the world no longer needed to worry about the economic future of developing countries.[1] By 1978, *The Wall Street Journal* was writing a front page feature saying: "There isn't anything left in the Green Revolution's bag of tricks. The Revolution, in fact, has turned against itself."[2]

Examples which illustrate this statement can be produced. In Madian-Salagnac in southern Haiti, an aid-funded hybrid corn station is developing Eto Amarillo corn for use by peasant farmers. The corn spoils after only three months of storage and cannot be used to make mayai moulin — a local staple. Less than a kilometre down the road, innovative subsistent farmers are equalling the hybrid maize yields with open-pollinated cultivars.[3] In Kitui, Kenya, farmers are working together to rejuvenate endangered traditional land races. For them, the new cereals are simply too expensive.[4] Near Quezon City in the Philippines, small landholders attend seminars on the costs and risks of the Green Revolution.[5] University agronomists in Tunisia are wondering what will happen to useful traditional food crops, as they are now being replaced by imported European seeds.[6] At Puebla, just outside of Mexico City, an alternative maize breeding programme is offering poor farmers open-pollinated seed that matches the productivity of CIMMYT varieties.[7] In Pakistan, angry rice farmers joke that the "miracle rice has led to miracle locusts".[8]

However, proponents of the Green Revolution argue that it has now entered its second phase. According to Henry Romney, Director of Information for the Rockefeller Foundation: "Much of the criticisms of the past few years have been accepted. The critics have turned us around".[9] Indeed, it would appear that Green Revolution scientists are looking increasingly to local crops (vegetable and fruit); and that the emphasis is changing to breeding for hardiness characteristics. Some wonder, though, if it is not too late to turn the 'revolution' around.

Origins

Bettina Conn has traced the Green Revolution back to the passage of the Bracero Law, restricting 'stoop labour' from Mexico entering the USA.[10] Seed companies moved to Mexico, Conn suggested, to take advantage of the labour opportunities there. Others saw a closer connection with the excess supply created in the fertilizer industry in the sixties, and the subsequent demand for new markets. The fact that the Kellogg Foundation has been an active participant in the CGIAR (which controls the IBPGR and the international crop research stations), was described as a sign of this connection[11]; because it was 'Kellogg' which developed the revolutionary process that created the fertilizer excess.[12] John W. Mellor, then Chief Economist for the US State Department's Agency for International Development, once described the Indian programme for the Green Revolution as "primarily a fertilizer scheme."[13] Certainly fertilizer companies and their foundations have long been active in promoting the 'revolution'.

The history of the Green Revolution, in fact, demonstrates the extensive involvement of major family foundations. The world's premier maize and wheat research facility, the CIMMYT, got underway in Mexico in 1943 with the financial support of the Rockefeller Foundation. The 'Fords' became involved in 1956, when the family foundation launched its Indian programme. The two foundations worked together in the early sixties to create the IRRI — the International Rice Research Institute — in the Philippines.[14] As successes and costs mounted, they were joined by the Kellogg Foundation and attempted to transfer responsibility for the entire 'revolution' to the UN. Robert McNamara — an old Ford Foundation board member and President of the World Bank — orchestrated an appropriate consortium of national governments, UN agencies and foundations to take over the funding. The CGIAR was the result. The foundations successfully shifted the financial burden, while maintaining considerable influence within the CGIAR. For example, all but one of the international crop research station directors have come up through the 'foundations'.[15]

Table 7
Support to International Crop Research Stations

Centre	Location	Date of Initiation	Proposed Budget for 1979 (US $000)
IRRI (International Rice Research Institute)	Los Banos, Philippines	1959	$13,503
CIMMYT (International Maize and Wheat Improvement Centre)	El Batan, Mexico	1964*	13,775
CIAT (International Centre for Tropical Agriculture)	Palmira, Colombia	1968	13,750
IITA (International Institute of Tropical Agriculture)	Ibadan, Nigeria	1965	14,480
CIP (International Potato Centre)	Lima, Peru	1972	7,412
ICRISAT (International Crops Research Institute for the Semi-Arid Tropics)	Hyderabad, India	1972	9,004
WARDA (West African Rice Development Association)	Monrovia, Liberia	1971	2,334
ICARDA (International Centre for Agricultural Research in Dry Areas)	Lebanon	—	11,976
IBPGR** (International Board for Plant Genetic Resources)	FAO, Rome, Italy	1973	2,720
		TOTAL:	$88,954

* Predecessor began in 1943.

** Included although not a research station.

Source: World Bank, 1979.

Related Achievements

The research stations and their highly-qualified staffs have been very influential. Not only can the CIMMYT boast a 'father of the Green Revolution' in Norman Borlaug, but CIMMYT wheat now grows on over 30 million acres around the globe; and wheat research is conducted on 1,140 plots in 65 countries. In addition, CIMMYT maize can be found on 289 test plots in 48 countries.[16] In its first decade, the IRRI has offered Asian rice farmers five major new varieties, and can claim to have had an overwhelming impact on Asian rice farming. As a result of these successes, financial support has been found for six other research stations — as well as two livestock research programmes — under the CGIAR auspices.

Their successes have produced more than financial benefits. Cereal yields in Turkey, since 1970, have doubled to 18 million tons per annum.[17] In the Punjab, two million acres are now sown in 'mexipak', or other improved local varieties.[18] Due to 'revolution' technology, Mexican wheat yields have leapt from 12 to 50 wheat bushels per acre.[19] The CIMMYT's new multi-line wheat has potential significance for farmers throughout the world.[20] By 1972-73, new high-yielding varieties (HYVs) were contributing a billion dollars a year to Asian cereal harvests.[21] With such impressive figures, the Green Revolution has won itself many supporters.

4.2 Criticisms

Sir Otto Frankel once described the Green Revolution as "a flood of vast dimensions".[22] The impact of the 'revolution' has indeed been overwhelming, but not all the related achievements have been necessarily worthy of praise:

Social Impact

Arthur Moser — President of the Agricultural Development Council founded by John D. Rockefeller III — argued early in the Green Revolution, that the co-operative social structure evident in many agrarian communities needed to be dismantled in order to encourage "aggressive interest in the market place".[23] Perhaps more than anything else, 'revolution' critics were confounded by the staggering arrogance common to many HYV architects. From the beginning, Western foundations, governments and scientists automatically assumed that the Third World needed only to duplicate the farming practices of the First World to achieve food self-sufficiency. This assumption was so all pervasive in planning and breeding that most failed to notice it. Others, like Moser, actively worked to adjust the social fabric to comply with scientific and marketing objectives. W. David Hopper provided a devastating analysis of the impact of the Green Revolution on Third World politics. He concluded a 1977 speech on the "Politics of Food" by saying: "The politics of the control of wealth is always an unseemly affair...a particularly inelegant diplomacy".[24] This properly sums up the impact he described for the Green Revolution.

The Chemical Connection

Staff at the CIMMYT would readily admit that much of the increased yield surrounding the revolution is due to the heavy application of fertilizers and herbicides.[25] One World Bank spokesman recently suggested that between 75 and 90 billion pounds of Asian rice are directly dependent upon Middle East petroleum.[26] Lester Brown claimed in 1967, that if Third World fertilizer demand could reach one-quarter of the per acre application of Japanese farmers, the USA could up its fertilizer exports from US $1 billion per annum to US $7 billion.[27] This statement came in a year when India was already paying out an equivalent of 20% of its export earnings on fertilizer imports. When cheap energy vanished in the early '70s, the Third World was saddled with an energy-dependent agricultural system. Fertilizer shortages in 1974 meant a loss of 15 million tons of grain — which is enough to feed 90 million people.[28]

Biocide requirements are at least as severe. Although 97% of the world's four billion pounds of pesticides manufactured each year come from the industrialized nations, the Third World consumes between 10 and 20% of this — and its share is growing rapidly.[29] From a Third World consumption of 160,000 tons in the early '70s, the FAO projects a rise to over 800,000 tons by the mid-eighties.[30] Pesticides are required partly because of the uniformity of new high-yielding crops, and partly because of their emphasis — as the name implies — on 'high yield' at some cost to disease-resistance. Non-governmental voluntary agencies have the costs of agrichemical inputs well documented in their files. In the seventies, aid requests frequently included additional dollar requirements to pay for chemical imports in order to maintain crop production.

Some, like the *US News and World Report*, positively welcomed the move to agrichemical supports: "One of the most important changes was an increased demand for US farm tools, fertilizers, pesticides, irrigation pumps and other agricultural equipment."[31] The Green Revolution has been undeniably profitable for agribusiness. By the sixties, agricultural enterprises were in need of a new market to maintain their growth. Bilateral and multilateral aid programmes made expansion into the Third World financially possible. Twenty years later, major agrichemical firms have achieved a worldwide distribution system able to market successfully in Asia, Africa and Latin America. The Green Revolution was the vehicle that made all this possible.

Quality Loss

Dr. L.W. Crowder of Ithaca, New York has pointed out a major shortcoming of the 'revolution' often overlooked by critics: "Small landholders usually practise a system of multi-cropping. For example, a mixture of corn and beans where they are adapted. Unfortunately, plant breeders have not taken into consideration the plant characteristics that favour growing crops together. Thus, new varieties of corn and bean do not grow well in combination."[32] Other experts have calculated that such companion-planting can increase both yield and profitability by more than 50%.[33] Beyond yield, companion-planting makes a major contribution to the protein production of subsistent farmers. Legume crops, cultivated in this way, are often kept by the family while the cereal crop is sold. Now, not only do the new varieties not grow well in combination, but the old varieties have often disappeared.

Crop Loss

Accompanying the failure to breed for companion-planting, Dr. G.J.H. Grubben of the Royal Tropical Institute in Amsterdam would add the general failure to take proper account of the nutritional and economic importance of all family-grown vegetable crops.[34] The statistical data on agricultural production focuses on commercial and/or cereals production, excluding subsistent farming and urban gardens. Therefore, vegetables are largely overlooked. Grubben notes that the Third World contributes substantially to the world's US $25 billion in vegetable production, but even this has not attracted the concern of Green Revolution scientists.[35]

Garrison Wilkes points out that half of the Third World's protein comes from food legumes: "The current dependence upon legumes makes doubly tragic their displacement by the Green Revolution wheats."[36] Wilkes goes on to report that the chickpea acreage in India has dropped to half that of wheat in the past two decades — historically, the two crops were equal. Wheat's increase, Wilkes claims, "was not because there was less dietary need for vegetable protein sources — but less profit."[37] With no more than a passing reference in crop yearbooks, high-protein (20-30%) legume crops are being replaced by low-protein (7-14%) grain crops. Michael Perelman suggests that per capita legume production in India dropped by 38% between 1961 and 1972 because grain varieties were highly subsidized, making legumes less attractive. The plus side of the Green Revolution with its increased yields has yet to be weighed against its minus side in lost protein.[38]

Poor Performance

As Dr. Norman Myers and Dr. Norman Baas make clear, the Green Revolution varieties have had their problems. A farmers' co-operative in the Philippines recently wrote to complain that the rice yields achieved on test plots at the International Rice Research Institute bear no relation to the achieved yields in farmers' fields. The difference has been as much as 8 tons per hectare at the IRRI, compared to 1.75 tons in farmers' fields. The farmers added: "Traditional varieties with more disease-resistant strains are known to equal, if not better, the yield per hectare (of IRRI rice) without the need for commercial fertilizers and other dangerous chemicals."[39]

While some new HYVs have not lived up to expectations, others have not lived at all. In 1973-74, Bengali farmers lost 80% of their rice crop, plus seedlings for the next crop, when they planted — as per instructions — new semi-dwarf rice in the river delta. High water destroyed the crop where the old varieties might have survived.[40] A year later, Indonesian farmers lost a half million acres of rice to leafhopper insects.[41] According to D.J. Dalrymple of the Agricultural Development Council in the USA: "In 1972, Brazil lost half its national (wheat) crop when it was attacked by a non-Mexican disease it was not bred to withstand."[42]

As the old varieties disappear, and as genetic uniformity spreads in the Third World, we will hear more and more about sudden, devastating crop disasters. Professor M. Dambroth brings erosion back to the doorstep of the HYVs: "...to a rather large extent, genetic erosion is a result of the Green Revolution."[43] His sentiments are echoed a few thousand miles away by Asian rice farmers: "We are even afraid that in the next five to ten years we will lose all our traditional rice seeds."[44] The 'revolution' has not so much offered farmers 'high-yielding varieties' as 'high-responding varieties' (HRVs). Given ideal conditions, and large amounts of fertilizers and chemicals, Green Revolution seeds will respond well and provide high yields. However, if any required inputs do not arrive on time, or are absent altogether, farmers may experience extensive crop failures.

Who Benefits?

Who has benefited most from the Green Revolution? When the Ford Foundation established its Intensive Agricultural Assistance Programme two decades ago, the target farm group ranked in the middle-class.[45] The prevailing theory of the day was that only middle-class farmers could take the risk involved and would show the creativity to respond to new technology. Perelman reported how this particular theory operated in Pakistan: "A World Bank study estimates that for each tractor purchased in Pakistan, between 7.5 and 11.8 full-time jobs are lost... After the purchase of a tractor the average farm size increased by 240% within three years, mostly through the eviction of tenants."[46] Employment per cultivated acre dropped by 40%. Estimates for Indonesia concluded that only 25% of peasant farmers benefited in any way from the 'revolution'. Back in Mexico, where it all began, Rockefeller Foundation staff candidly admitted that their work has done little to aid the poor.[47] In fact, this type of agricultural development resulted in increased urbanization as the poor were driven from their fields and forced into the cities, to buy expensive cereals grown in fields where they once harvested inexpensive legumes.

Within the space of two decades, the varied agricultural systems of the Third World and their surrounding social structures have been uprooted, overthrown and replaced by a new Western model. Both the crops and economies of Asia, Africa and Latin America have been hauled into the Western market economy under the pretext of feeding the hungry. The Third World is being brought into a food system which has not worked well in the First

World, and which is in imminent danger of destroying alternative options for poor nations. This particular road to hell has been paved with more than good intentions. Speaking of the early phases of the Green Revolution, Bettina Conn reported: "At the same time, representatives of the Institute (IRRI) were advising US agribusiness firms and farm machinery companies to investigate the potential of investing in these less developed tropical farm areas."[48] The IRRI's message did not fall on deaf ears.

Key to the market potential of Third World commodities is seed. International agribusiness began controlling the 'seed end' of the Green Revolution fairly early in its history. Although Borlaug's HYVs were developed with government and foundation financing, and although their multiplication was controlled by Mexico's National Promotion Agency for Seeds through co-operative seed grower associations, much of the external trade in HYVs fell to global companies. Writing in *Merchants of Grain*, Dan Morgan reported: "... but as the demand for Mexican seed increased, several co-operatives and at least one private company began producing certified seed. Mexican banks financed some of the development but Cargill and Continental began making 'forward' arrangements with farmers and co-operatives for seeds ... in this way, private companies often had a 'call' on a substantial amount of the miracle wheat from Mexico, still the world's leading supplier of high-yielding seeds." Morgan went on to relate an incident whereby Cargill and Continental had a 'corner' on Mexico's HVVs in 1977 and succeeded in outmanoeuvring a number of European seed traders.[49] When HYVs ostensibly moved from being government-funded out into a buyers' market, they became sources of market speculation and profit for agribusiness.

Table 8
Global HYV Seed Requirements — 1980

Crop	% Increase Over 1974	Tons of Seed Required
Rice	50%	230,000
Wheat	60%	700,000
Corn	40%	200,000
Sorghum & Millet	20%	45,000

Source: Background documentation for the World Food Conference, Rome, 1974.

*　　　*　　　*

If you control the seed, you are a long way to controlling the entire food system: what crops will be grown; what inputs will be used; and, where the products will be sold. At the Rome Food Conference, FAO experts projected the world's HYV seed requirements for 1980. (Table 8) The increases contemplated meant enormous market potential for agribusiness. Control of the world seed industry would be the second phase of the Green Revolution.

REFERENCES

1. Perelman, M., *Farming for Profit in a Hungry World.* Landmark Series, 1977, p. 143.

2. *The Wall Street Journal.* June 14, 1972, p. 1.

3. Information derived from an unpublished report by Gerald Balcan, which was received as a project proposal in February, 1979.

4. From a letter from Noel Mondejar of the Farmers Assistance Board, Inc. in the Phillipines dated November 18, 1978.

5. Information provided in project reports via Trocaire in Dublin.

6. From a letter from Dr. Jamil Mustaga dated November 13, 1978.

7. From a letter from Dr. David Barkin dated January 10, 1979.

8. Allaby, M., "Miracle Rice Breeds Miracle Locusts", *Ecologist.*

9. Perelman, M., op. cit., p. 161.

10. "Seed Monopoly", *Elements.* February 1975, pp. 6-7. Bettina Conn actually prepared the article, but was not designated author when it was printed in the magazine. She is, nevertheless, referred to in the text.

11. Wade, N., "International Agricultural Research", in Abelson, P.H. ed., *Food: Politics, Economics, Nutrition and Research.* 1975, p. 95.

12. Perelman, M., op. cit., p. 170.

13. Ibid., p. 169.

14. Wade, N., op. cit., p. 91.

15. Ibid., p. 91.

16. Dalrymple, D.J., "Impact of the International Institutes on Crop Production". An article prepared for the Agricultural Development Council in January, 1975.

17. Peters, C., "The Browning of the Green Revolution", *Country Guide.* p. 18.

18. Frankel, O.H. ed., *Survey of Crop Genetic Resources in their Centres of Diversity.* FAO, February 1973, p. 21.

19. Crowder, L.W., "Genetics and a Hungry World", *New York's Food and Life Sciences Quarterly.* Vol. 11 No. 2, 1978, p. 13.

20. Dalrymple, D.J., op. cit..

21. Wade, N., op. cit., p. 92.

22. Frankel, O.H., "Genetic Conservation: Why and How". An undated speech made in Canberra, Australia. p. 17.

23. Perelman, M., op. cit., p. 146.

24. Hopper, W.D., "The Politics of Food". A speech made to a symposium on 'Canada and World Food' held in Ottawa, August 22-24, 1977. p. B-3-9.

25. Peters, C., op. cit., p. 18.

26. Perelman, M., op. cit., p. 146.

27. Ibid., p. 170.

28. Ibid., p. 174.

29. *The World Food Problem* UN World Food Conference, November 1974, p. 49.

30. Ibid., p. 49.

31. "Seed Monopoly", *Elements.* February 1975, pp. 6-7.

32. Crowder, L.W., op. cit., p. 13.

33. Dalrymple, D.J., op. cit..

34. Grubben, G.J.H., *Tropical Vegetables and their Genetic Resources*. IBPGR, 1977, pp. 7-8.

35. Ibid., p. 7.

36. Wilkes, G., "Native Crops and Wild Food Plants", *Ecologist*. Vol. 7 No. 8, p. 315.

37. Ibid., p. 313.

38. Perelman, M., op. cit., p. 151.

39. From correspondence and enclosures from Noel Mondejar dated November 18, 1978.

40. Perelman, M., op. cit., p. 156.

41. Ibid., p. 155.

42. Dalrymple, D.J., op. cit..

43. From an October 27, 1978 letter from M. Dambroth.

44. From correspondence and enclosures from Noel Mondejar dated November 18, 1978.

45. Perelman, M., op. cit., p. 145.

46. Ibid., p. 149.

47. Ibid., p. 144.

48. "Seed Monopoly", *Elements*. February 1975, pp. 6-7.

49. Morgan, D., *Merchants of Grain*. Viking, 1979, pp. 240-1.

Chapter 5

The Seed Revolution

The global seed trade is one of the fastest growing, most profitable industries in the food chain... There is a strong world-wide interdependence in many important seed species... As a result of its profitability and favourable outlook, a number of large multinational companies have acquired, or are considering, acquisitions within the seed trade. Leading this activity is a group of major pharmaceutical, chemical, petroleum and food concerns.
— L. William Teweles & Co., 1978.

The seed industry cannot develop alone. The users of good seeds must also have inputs such as fertilizers, pesticides, machinery and water... The marketing of seeds is frequently handled through the same channels used for other inputs. Special consideration is needed on how to market all inputs more effectively through common channels.
— *Seed Industry Development*, FAO, 1976.

In the Philippines... Esso developed a network of 100 'agroservice centres' where farmers could purchase seed, pesticides and farm implements as well as fertilizers from the Esso dealer.
— Michael Perelman, *Farming for Profit in a Hungry World*, USA, 1977.

In less than three years alone, the cost of certified, high-yielding seeds here has gone up almost 100%.
— Farmers Assistance Board, Inc., The Philippines, 1978.

Successful plant breeding is dependent upon many variables: soils, precipitation, growing seasons, insect and animal life can vary from kilometre to kilometre, significantly influencing the specific crop variety to be grown. Nevertheless, a business consulting firm, L. William Teweles & Co., is producing *The Global Seed Study* as a resource for governments and multinational enterprises on the assumption that seed is now a world-wide industry.[1] Teweles & Co. recognizes that all the world survives on a few major crops: maize can be grown from Canada to Tanzania; soybeans are found around global temperate zones; and, wheat is everywhere. Company plant breeders may have to do considerable genetic adjustment for each market area, but once they have begun to develop a specific crop, they can expect world-wide sales.

The groundwork for the global seed industry was laid by the Green Revolution, and the multilateral and bilateral aid programmes which supported it. For example, HYV chemical requirements allowed agrichemical firms to establish a global sales infrastructure heavily subsidized by governments. 'Phase II' logically evolved with the turning over of the seed programme to private enterprise — the multinational pharmaceutical, chemical and petroleum outfits identified by Teweles & Company.

5.1   Elements of Phase II

Two movements developed simultaneously in the early sixties. Beginning in 1957, the FAO launched a World Seed Campaign culminating in World Seed Year in 1961.[2] At the same time, an intensive campaign to permit patent-equivalent protection for new varieties began achieving success in Europe. World Seed Year came to a climax on December 2, 1961, when the International Convention for the Protection of New Varieties of Plants came into being. 'Plant breeders' rights' (PBR), or 'plant variety protection', made it possible for the first time for private breeders to receive royalty payments on newly developed varieties, and to control the spread of their patented varieties. Previously, the lack of 'patent' protection had discouraged large-scale corporate interest.

Although 'patent' systems for plants are currently being explored in several Third World nations, private breeders have only lately seen any need for this protection in developing countries. Operating under a multitude of names — certificates of invention, leases, rights or licenses — they have generally afforded companies all the protection required in the Third World. The key to the overseas market for Western multinationals has been the spread of HYVs; and the resulting farmer-dependence upon new seeds and chemicals. In the First World, however, 'patents' have long been considered essential for the safe conduct of business and the control of crop varieties. Much more important than royalty payments, patents offer private enterprise an opportunity to govern the market.[3]

The FAO's Seed Improvement and Development Programme

Early in 1978, the FAO's Seed Improvement and Development Programme (SIDP) counselled Third World policy-makers: "While the government always has an important role in the development of the seed programme, it would not be monopolistic or exclusive. Participation of the non-government sector in seed production and marketing should be actively encouraged through initiatives such as special credit, tax concessions, lease purchase arrangements for facilities and equipment, low rental land, technical assis-

48

tance, relaxation of restrictions on land holding and accessibility to basic seed stocks of publicly-developed cultivars."[4] While excluding quality control management, the SIDP has taken a firm stand in promoting the global seed industry. In a 1976 report, the SIDP suggested: "Farmers should be supplied, as soon as possible, with a package of balanced inputs including quality seeds, fertilizers, water, plant protection chemicals and machinery in order to obtain higher yields."[5] This 'package' approach — so important to the global seed industry — has been a source of concern for many scientists.[6]

The SIDP also deals with the possibility of plant patent legislation in the Third World: "As a way to encourage private research, some provision for breeders' rights legislation often has been made. Whether or not this need exist in a particular country would need review."[7] The report goes on to ask: "Does the existing system encourage or discourage private research activities? Would breeders' rights legislation have any value in the present or future seed programme?"[8] The report lists the International Seed Testing Association as a source for further advice.[9]

The SIDP has been at the forefront in terms of encouraging Third World governments to subsidize agrichemical inputs and basic seed prices. At one point in the Green Revolution, Michael Perelman noted: "The World Bank estimates that about half of all purchases in the Third World were financed through government aid programmes."[10] At times the subsidy system created problems as well as opportunities. Dr. P.H. Nelson and A. Kuhn of the private West German seed multinational, KWS AG, told a 1973 International Seeds Symposium that: "Governments often link seed prices to cheap food prices. This makes it difficult for the private sector. Of necessity, private seed firms would have to raise the selling price above the subsidized level to cover their costs. With the price of the end product being officially controlled, it is highly questionable whether seed prices can be increased without considerably decreasing the demand for improved seed." KWS, however, had a solution: "A necessary alternative would be for governments to develop a policy of supporting the intended private industry."[11]

KWS — which is a dominant seed company in Europe, with American interests — gave the 1973 FAO-sponsored symposium a helpful review of the Green Revolution's phases: "... direct seed imports were largely regarded as a short-term rather than as a long-term solution. With rising demand, the import of certified seed of improved varieties started to contribute a drain on the stock of scarce foreign currency. In addition, imported varieties occasionally failed to produce the expected yields, because they were bred for environmental conditions which differed from those of the importing countries. Consequently, an increasing number of developing countries undertook to establish their own national seed industries."[12] Nelson and Kuhn continued: "The strategy frequently adopted to achieve this end envisages private foreign seed companies to participate in this effort through the establishment of joint ventures with local investors."[13]

With the encouragement of the SIDP, 'phase II' of the Green Revolution is being turned over to agribusiness. The American Seed Trade Association, for example, is organizing a consortium of 42 US firms to expand seed sales in several countries including Korea, South and Central America. D. Kenneth

King of Northrup-King (a US seed giant, now owned by Sandoz of Switzerland), has commented: "Foreign markets are opening slowly but they are extremely attractive."[14]

The international market is indeed attractive to seed companies. However, the reverse may not be true — at least for the Third World. Staff Discussion Paper 2, prepared for the US 'President's Commission on World Hunger', offers a review of the contributions US corporations might make towards solving the world's food problems. In an otherwise favourable commentary there are two substantial shortcomings, best summarized by Cary Fowler: "(Multinational agribusinesses) don't know how to distribute food to the poor."[15] The paper notes: "... large, centralized US corporations have little experience, expertise or even interest when it comes to marketing products to low-income, highly-dispersed consumers with foreign habits and tastes."[16]

Corporate expertise lies in the area of export agriculture and forages. Bettina Conn undoubtedly agrees that this analysis is as applicable to the seed industry as it is to any other part of agribusiness: "Vitally needed agricultural land in India now produces soybean seed for export by US companies to the London market."[17] The SIDP is obviously not a malevolent monster. However, it does seem confused and is often at variance with other parts of the FAO. For example, its advice on the role of the private seed industry in developing countries is poorly conceived — raising questions about the overall capability of the programme.

The Trade Associations

SIDP's apparent confusion has been a source of dissatisfaction for the seed industry. At a 1973 symposium in Vienna, H.H. Leenders of the FIS — Fédération Internationale des Semences — took time from his speech to advise the FAO that their members "strongly criticized" SIDP's guidelines relating to plant breeders' rights.[18] Leenders may have been thinking of a manual on cereal seeds production, quality control and distribution, edited by W. P. Feistritzer, which raised doubts about the merits of patent protection.[19] In fact, at the same Vienna symposium, Feistritzer presented a study of Third World seed development programmes which made it clear to all that any patent system would have a negative impact.

The FIS is one of two international organizations, created for the seed industry, that has long lobbied for patent rights. It shares this history with the International Seed Testing Association (ISTA). The two organizations got underway in the 1920s; and co-operate closely through the European and Mediterranean Plant Protection Organization (EPPO), and the International Association of Breeders for the Protection of Breeders' Rights (ASSINSEL). Liaison work with governments and UN agencies is a primary task of the trade associations; and these days, the 'patent' question represents their major issue.

The Patent Administrators

International conventions seem to be the stuff and substance of patents. They represent the long, slow construction of international legal codes protecting inventions — a process that traces as far back as Venice in the fifteenth century.[20] In a world where technology is the road to profits and patents the guarantee of technological control, WIPO — the World Intellectual Properties Organization — stands in the centre of some of the most financially important legal wrangles ever seen in the law courts. To record and process the one million patent documents sent its way each year, WIPO enlists INPADOC — the International Patent Documentation Centre.[21] WIPO became the UN's fourteenth agency in 1974; and in its wake, UPOV — the Union for the Protection of New Varieties of Plants — joined the UN system in a semi-official position.[22]

The majority of WIPO's 106 members are developing countries. WIPO offers a 'Permanent Programme for Development Co-operation', including regular regional symposia directed to Third World government officials; and in addition, provides 'model laws' for developing countries related to inventions and designs. The Director-General of WIPO also carries the title of Secretary-General of UPOV[23]; and although WIPO's 'model laws' advise against 'patenting' plant varieties, they do encourage breeders to consider the UPOV 'plant breeders' rights' alternative.[24]

'Patent' or 'Right'?

The fine distinction between a 'patent' and a 'right' escapes many, if not most, policy-makers. According to UPOV: "Certain difficulties had to be overcome since the system of protection of technical inventions caused and still cause special problems when applied to living substances."[25] A general UPOV brochure goes on to explain that "in reality one single plant is not like any other". UPOV admits that an intense debate exists on some basic terminology surrounding plants — such as 'plant variety'.[26] The reality of the situation is that ultimate ownership cannot be shown with regard to higher-order living things. Therefore, since plants are unable to fulfill the requirements for 'patents', an alternative had to be found — i.e. plant breeders' rights. With laudable humility UPOV concedes that its 'convention', "does not solve all the problems."[27] However, UPOV does talk of plant protection on a worldwide scale.[28]

According to Feistritzer: "Membership in the union (UPOV) is of little significance unless the whole seed industry of a country (plant breeding, seed production, quality control and marketing) is highly developed."[29] Yet, neither Feistritzer nor the SIDP could be considered anti-plant breeders' rights. By 1976, Feistritzer was advising Third World policy-makers of the numerous reasons for improving the seed industry and expanding the participation of the private sector: "Farmers will require other manufactured goods; nationally, a seed industry can give a high return on a relatively low investment; the seed industry is probably the best catalyst for expanding the agricultural marketing system within a country and may equally be a stimulous to foreign trade; seed is an international commodity and, perhaps, more than any other, moves across national boundaries."[30] Feistritzer added that private seed industry participation in the Third World has not been "too successful",

51

but cited political and economic reasons.[31] He concluded his commentary on private enterprise by saying: "Private plant breeders in particular might be more encouraged to allow their varieties to be used when assured of such a right."[32]

*   *   *

It seems clear that two parallel movements are coming together on a global scale: the Green Revolution moving to private enterprise; and, the spread of patent-equivalent legislation. A closer look at the enterprises behind these movements and the implications of PBR legislation — for both First and Third World countries — is now in order.

REFERENCES

1. From a 'Prospectus' circulated by L. Wm. Teweles & Co. in October, 1978 to potential buyers of *The Global Seed Study*.

2. Feistritzer, W.P. ed., *Seed Industry Development: A Guide to Planning, Decision-Making and Operation of Seed Programmes and Projects*. FAO, 1976, p. iv.

3. *UPOV*. General Information Brochure, Publication No. 408 (E), 1976.

4. *SIDP: The FAO Seed Improvement and Development Programme*. FAO, January 1978, p. 4.

5. Feistritzer, W.P. ed., op. cit., p. iii.

6. Crowder, L.W., "Genetics and a Hungry World", *New York's Food and Life Sciences Quarterly*. Vol. 11 No. 8, 1978, p. 16.

7. Feistritzer, W.P. ed., op. cit., p. 42.

8. Ibid., p. 43.

9. Ibid., p. 15.

10. Perelman, M., *Farming for Profit in a Hungry World*. Landmark Series, 1977, p. 171.

11. Nelson, P.H. and Kuhn, A., "Recent Organizational Development and Future Trends in Seed Production and Marketing — Private Sector", *The Role of Seed Science Technology in Agricultural Development*. FAO, 1973, p. 212.

12. Ibid., p. 209.

13. Ibid., p. 211.

14. "Seed Monopoly", *Elements*. February 1975, pp. 6-7.

15. From a speech made by Cary Fowler to Saskatchewan farmers in February, 1979.

16. *Staff Discussion Paper No. 2*. US 'President's Commission on World Hunger', Undated, p. 10.

17. "Seed Monopoly", *Elements*. February 1975, pp. 6-7.

18. Leenders, H.H., "Statement of International Seed Trade Federation (FIS)", *The Role of Seed Science Technology in Agricultural Development*. FAO, 1973, p. 382.

19. Ibid., p. 381.

20. *WIPO*. General Information Brochure, Publication No. 400 (E), 1978, p. 46.

21. Ibid., p. 42.

22. Ibid., p. 1.

23. *UPOV*. General Information Brochure, Publication No. 408 (E), 1976, p. 11.

24. *Model Laws for Inventions*. WIPO, 1975, p. 23.

25. *UPOV*. General Information Brochure, Publication No. 408 (E), 1976, p. 11.

26. Ibid., p. 6.

27. Ibid., p. 11.

28. Ibid., p. 33.

29. *Cereal Seed Technology: A Manual for Cereal Seed Production, Quality Control and Distribution*. FAO, 1975, p. 24.

30. Feistritzer, W.P. ed., op. cit., p. 28.

31. Ibid., p. 111.

32. Ibid., p. 29.

Chapter 6

The New Seedsmen

*In fact, for multinational corporations, seed lends itself to world-wide commer-
cialization ... the successful international operations of present industry leaders
lends credibility to the potential for world-wide seed organizations.*
— L. Wm. Teweles & Co., 1976.

*The purpose of plant breeders' rights legislation for Canada will be to stimulate the
production of crop varieties so that Canadian agriculture can produce to the maxi-
mum to help feed the hungry.*
— W.T. Bradnock, Agriculture Canada, 1977.

We are, in fact, selling our birthright for a mess of pottage.
— Sir Joseph Hutchinson, Oxford, UK, 1976.

6.1   The "Acquirers' Romance"

In a 1978 letter to prospective buyers of *The Global Seed Study*, L.
William Teweles & Co. wrote: "In the last ten years, at least 30 seed companies
with sales of $5 million or more have been acquired by large, non-seed multi-
national corporate enterprises. At least eleven more such mergers are believed
to be under discussion."[1] This was actually an underestimate. According to
Agriculture Canada's Wilf Bradnock, who was working for the UK government at the time, in the week that PBR legislation was passed in the United
Kingdom, one company — Ranks Hovis McDougall — bought out 84
county supply companies. By the time its spree was over, the company had
acquired over 100 firms and was well on its way to becoming a giant in the seed
retail industry.[2] Acquisitions were so extensive following passage of the Plant
Variety Protection Act in the USA at the end of 1970, that the American Seed
Trade Association devoted half of its annual meeting to a special symposium
called, "How to Sell your Seed Company".[3] This "acquirers' romance with the
seed industry", as Teweles & Co. described it, was neither a mystery nor a surprise to those familiar with PBR.[4]

The suitors in this 'romance' are mainly multinational agrichemical
companies; not merely agribusiness concerns, but companies who draw their
primary profits from pharmaceuticals or petroleum-based chemicals. There

55

are exceptions like ITT, Anderson Clayton and Cargill; but the industry appears to be dominated by the likes of Ciba-Geigy, Sandoz, Pfizer, Upjohn, Monsanto, Union Carbide and Royal Dutch/Shell. According to *Business Week*, with seed industry profits growing at an annual return rate of 19%: "Few US industries look forward to markets as strong as the seed industry."[5] With the advent of protection legislation in Europe, the USA and Japan, acquirers can expect to add royalty payments — on a global scale — to their profits. More importantly, protection allows dominant companies an opportunity to achieve market control in specific crops. As Teweles & Co. points out, the industry has historically been comprised of small private enterprises — ripe for take-over.[6] Jean-Pierre Berlan, a Research Fellow with the French Government's INRA — the national agricultural research institute — notes that the family-based seed industry in that country went from a host of small enterprises to an oligopoly with the advent of PBR.[7]

Why Agrichemical Interest?

If you are willing to pay US $25,000, a copy of *The Global Seed Study* may provide some of the answers as to why the special interest of chemical concerns in the seed industry. In the first place, the chemical industry has been particularly beset by health and safety issues since the late sixties. Old products, shown to be dangerous, are being removed from the market before the industry can recoup its research costs; and new products are subjected to rigorous testing spread over several years. Although less visible than the food additive and drug side of the chemical industry, agrichemicals have faced growing public scrutiny: concern that nitrogen fertilizers erode the ozone layer and increase skin cancer; that some biocides cause mutations in both crops and people; and, fears that biocide residues will build up in the body, thereby increasing the cancer risk. All these concerns contribute to making a jittery industry with fickle investors. Teweles & Co. notes: "In contrast with many other farm suppliers the seed industry has largely avoided attack by consumer, ecological and regulatory bodies."[8] The study prospectus suggests that improved seed research would appeal to environmentalists, since better disease-resistant varieties could lead to a reduction in the use of chemicals.

At the risk of seeming contradictory, the prospectus later notes the potential for: "... seed coating and pelleting, utilizing the seed as a delivery system for chemicals and biologicals to the field."[9] The potential for actually increasing chemical consumption is great. A quick search through INPADOC's seed-related patent files shows that — among others — Upjohn, Union Carbide, Monsanto, Diamond Shamrock, ITT and Sandoz are all working in this area. For example, INPADOC registered '885342' — a "slow release soil fumigant" — back in 1969.[10]

Thirdly, the Teweles & Co. outline offers to bring its buyers up-to-date on: "...the past, present and projected direction of industry genetic research...The public sector's changing contribution is appraised. World-wide genetic sources, breeders' rights and emerging genetic technologies are discussed in appropriate detail."[11] According to investment researchers like Dain, Kalman & Quail, the seed industry itself is passé. The Minneapolis brokers speak only of a "genetics supply industry", in which they lump plants and animals with a disturbing disregard for Darwin.[12] Upjohn — through its centralized R&D (Research and Development) at Kalamazoo, and Fisons — through its unified research in the UK, are already reaping benefits from an integrated genetics approach. It appears that companies with a 'chemicals' background are the most likely candidates to move into seed genetics. As Malcolm Salter and Wolf Weinhold comment in the *Harvard Business Review*, companies are most likely to diversify "into businesses with similar marketing and distribution characteristics, similar production technologies or similar science-based research activities."[13] There is also the connection Teweles & Co. makes between genetic resources and breeders' rights. PBR — proprietary control over living plant material — gives essential investment protection to the 'genetics supply industry'; i.e. the control of genetic resources becomes important and germ plasm becomes a marketable commodity.

In other words, acquisitions in the seed industry might provide some profit protection to agrichemical firms besieged by government regulations and buyer resistance; i.e. if farmers use less biocides they may well require more acreage to grow the same quantities, meaning more seed sales. On the other hand, if the seed is a deliverer of chemicals, it might either reduce environmental damage and farmer health risk, or increase the use of chemicals substantially as farmers are offered (possibly without option) a 'package' deal of chemicals and seeds. Finally, PBR legislation — meaning variety control — would also mean control over genetic resources for future breeding. Whichever way one interprets the situation, the agrichemical companies cannot lose.

Table 9
US Plant Patent Domination*

Crop	Number and Names of Dominant Seed Company Buyers Involved	% Controlled
Bean	4 — Sandoz, Union Carbide, Upjohn, Purex	79
Cotton	4 — KWS, Pioneer, Southwide, Anderson Clayton	44
Lettuce	6 — Union Carbide, FMC, ITT, Upjohn, Purex, Celanese	66
Pea	2 — Sandoz, Upjohn	43
Soybean	8 — Sandoz, Upjohn, Purex, Shell/Olin, Pfizer, Kent, KWS, Pioneer	42
Wheat	8 — KWS, Ciba-Geigy, Dekalb, Sandoz, Cargill, FMC, Shell/Olin, Pioneer	34

* Of the 562 patent 'certificates' issued by the US Plant Variety Protection Office to March 1979, over 46% were issued to the dominant 17 firms who are the most active seed company buyers; only slightly over 9% were issued to State Universities and Agricultural Experimental Stations. Of all patents issued, 72% went to six crops where a handful of multinational firms clearly dominate the industry.

Source: Official record of the Plant Variety Protection Office, 1979.

For some, these points amount to a healthy, profit-conscious, environmentally-helpful approach to plant breeding. For others, the road appears to lead only to increased social costs. However, both sides agree that major changes are taking place in the seed industry; and no one denies the pre-eminence of agrichemical enterprises in the buying spree now underway. Neither the governments currently considering PBR legislation — Ireland, Canada and Australia — nor the seed industry itself have addressed this reality and its possible implications. At stake, in economic terms, is a US $10 billion industry (estimated 1978 global sales).[14] Corporate buyers have spent over US $200 million in recent years to buy control. In 1974 alone, over 4% of the US seed industry sold out.[15] It would seem reasonable for governments — First and Third World — to want to know more before taking on such pivotal legislation.

6.2   Who Are The New Seedsmen?

Following the merger trail in the seed industry is not easy. For example, of the 500 leading firms in the USA, only a handful are publicly-held. Moreover, the numbers involved disguise the dominant control of a few large companies over the whole industry. Seed corn in the USA, for instance, is by far the most important seed commodity, but roughly two-thirds of all sales flow to only four companies: Dekalb, Pioneer, Sandoz and Ciba-Geigy — with Dekalb and Pioneer controlling half the market. The same four companies, and their subsidiaries, dominate about 59% of the hybrid sorghum market in the United States. It is interesting to note that these companies — at least in hybrid corn — tend to sell in different regions, thereby facing little competition in their chosen territory.[16] Pioneer "is recognized as the largest corn research and development company in the world."[17] Sandoz's Northrup-King, involved in several major crops, has the largest sales volume in the USA.[18] In Europe, KWS has a dominant position regarding several crops. The global leader, however, appears to be Royal Dutch/Shell — the petroleum and chemical company headquartered in London and Amsterdam. This firm controls the destiny of thirty seed companies in Europe and North America. (Table 10)

Even the buyers are being bought. Olin Corporation of the USA — Royal Dutch/Shell's American partner in North American Plant Breeders (NAPB) — is being pursued by Celanese. Celanese, which has recently bought both Cepril and Moran Seeds, also produces fibres, chemicals and plastics. Besides a 40% share in NAPB, Olin can offer interests in chemicals, brass, fine paper, film, firearms and a home-building subsidiary. The two together would rank sixth in the US chemical industry, and have considerable influence in both seeds and agrichemicals.[19] A take-over of still greater proportions looms between the Friendrich Flick Group of Dusseldorf and W.R. Grace of the USA. Flick is trying for about a one-third share of Grace, which specializes in chemicals, fertilizers and natural resources.[20] Both firms are rumoured to be eyeing the seed industry for other possible mergers. Writing in *Chemical Age*, Phillip Hill records a merger on the other side of the Atlantic which has

Table 10
Royal Dutch/Shell Seed Interests

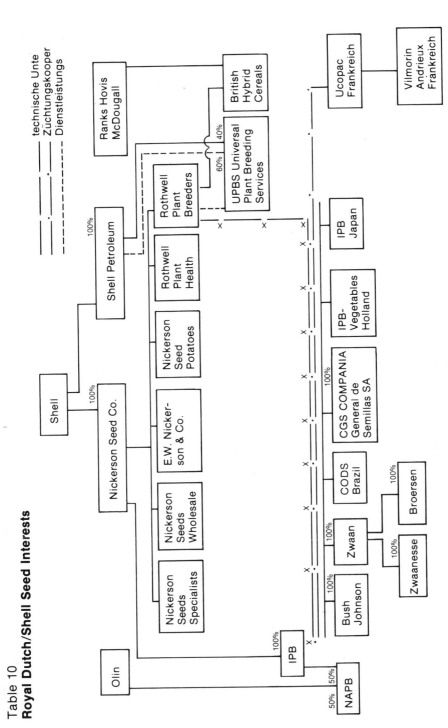

technische Unterstützung
Züchtungskooperation
Dienstleistungs

Source: Unpublished source.

created "one of the biggest fertilizer firms in Europe". Rhone-Poulenc has joined with PUK to acquire 61% of the capital of Sopag — the fertilizer group previously controlled by Gardinier. Once again, these agrichemical enterprises are thought to be looking ahead — i.e. to the world seed industry. Interestingly enough, Rhone-Poulenc and PUK beat out Dutch States Mines and Shell for Sopag.[21]

Table 11
Recent North American Seed Company Acquisitions

NEW OWNER	SEED COMPANY	NEW OWNER	SEED COMPANY
Anderson Clayton	Paymaster Farms	NAPB (Olin &	Agripro, Inc.
	Tomaco-Genetic	Royal Dutch/	
	Giant	Shell)	
Cargill	Dorman Seeds	Pioneer Hi-Bred	Lankhart
	Kroeker Seeds		Lockett
	PAG		Arnold Thomas
Celanese	Cepril Inc.		Seed Co.
	Moran Seeds		Petersons
	Harris Seeds	Pfizer	Clemens Seed Farms
Central Soya	O's Gold Seed Co.		Jordan Wholesale Co.
Ciba-Geigy	Funk Seeds Intern'l.		Trojan Seed Co.
	Stewart Seeds		Warwick Seeds
Diamond Shamrock	Taylor-Evans	Purex	Advanced Seeds
	Seed Co.		Ferry-Morse Seeds
FMC	Seed Research		Hulting Hybrids
	Association	Sandoz	National-NK
Garden Products	Gurney Seeds		Northrup-King
Hilleshoeg/Cardo	Intern'l. Forest		Rogers Brothers
	Seeds Co.	Southwide, Inc.	Delta Pineland
Intern'l. Multifoods	Baird Inc.	Tate & Lyle	Berger & Plate
	Lynk Bros.	Tejon Ranch Co.	Waterman-Loomis Co.
ITT	O.M. Scott & Sons	Union Carbide	Keystone Seed Co.
	Burpee Seeds		Jacques Seeds
Kent Feed Co.	Teweles Seed Co.		Amchem Products
KWS AG	Coker	Upjohn	Asgrow Seeds
Monsanto	Farmers' Hybrid Co.		

Sources: Newspapers and Private Sources.

It is also possible that some of the pressure towards consolidation of seed and agrichemical interests has come from the major petroleum companies who are eyeing both industries. Commenting on the 'chemicals' side in the spring of 1978, *Business Week* noted: "Further oil company involvement seems inevitable. Exxon, already a big producer, plans to move further downstream by means of an acquisition that could make it its first such test of the anti-trust climate." The article prophesized the same route for Standard Oil of California whose chemical subsidiary, Chevron, is already big in biocides.[22] Teweles & Co. would also add Occidental Petroleum — owner of Hooker Chemicals — to those oil giants looking to the seed industry.[23]

60

Table 12
Data: Agribusiness Seed Companies

Fortune Rank	Name	Sales US $ 000	Employees
252	Anderson Clayton	947,953	12,757
—	Cargill**	10,000,000	—
106	Celanese	2,320,000	32,100
115	Central Soya	2,177,385	9,500
52	Ciba-Geigy*	4,151,660	74,080
166	Diamond Shamrock	1,530,382	11,279
103	FMC	2,373,234	44,249
273	Intern'l. Multifoods	847,030	7,895
11	ITT	13,145,664	375,000
	Kent Feed Co.	70,000	400
44	Monsanto	4,594,500	61,519
174	Olin	1,472,500	22,000
126	Pfizer	2,031,925	40,200
397	Purex	491,219	7,100
1	Royal Dutch/Shell*	39,700,000	155,000
126	Sandoz*	1,993,348	35,605
118	Tate & Lyle*	2,143,116	20,015
	Tejon Ranch Co.	21,900	75
21	Union Carbide	7,036,100	113,669
217	Upjohn	1,134,325	18,830

* Company rank is based on *Fortune's* list of major industrial enterprises outside the USA.
** Cargill Inc. is a private enterprise.
Sources: *Fortune*, May 1978 and August 1978.

The acquisition pace may now be accelerating as global firms anticipate passage of restrictive varietal legislation in Australia, Ireland and Canada; and the entrance of more countries into the UPOV 'convention'. It bears repeating that the firms involved are global in scale and, therefore, look to the entire world for markets. For example, the influence of European firms is evident in the American market. Europe has had PBR for almost a decade longer than the USA, giving some continental firms a lead in the global industry. Discussions within the UN regarding a 'Code of Conduct for Transnational Corporations' have included the assumption that there exists certain areas of vital national concern too important to be left to the interests of multinationals.[24] Clearly, a nation's plant genetic resources and seed supply should fall within this category.

Implications for the Third World

Developing nations are often given technology 'packages' which they cannot refuse — at prices they cannot afford. A special 1974 UN study of this problem concluded that the Third World also tends to lose out with patent legislation. For example, India has attempted to set ceilings on royalty charges for imported technology, but found the effort next to useless.[25] Exporters have too many options open to them in the global market. Trademarks offer a classic non-patent example. Companies can approximate patent-control via advertising; then consumers ask for the brand name rather than the product type. Many Third World countries are concerned about this situation. For example, according to an UNCTAD Secretariat report, the Mexican Government proposed the banning of trademarks in 1976.[26]

6.3   The Significance of PBR

The opportunities available to the new seedsmen seem more than ample without PBR legislation. The Green Revolution has created global demand and facilitated corporate marketing systems. The R&D link between chemicals and seeds, by itself, would seem enough to stimulate aggressive interest in plant breeding. The primary role of seeds in the food chain and the global interdependence upon a few crops should be expected to guarantee multinational interest. Might not the technology of seed coating and the subsidies offered through foreign aid be greater impetus to the sweeping changes

Table 13
Dominant US Seed Companies

Crop	Dominant Firm(s)	Ultimate Owner
Corn	Pioneer Dekalb	
Alfalfa	Northrup-King Funk Pioneer	Sandoz Ciba-Geigy
Vegetables	Burpee Asgrow	ITT Upjohn
Sorghum	Cargill Funk Pioneer Asgrow	Sandoz Upjohn
Grass	Vaughn Jacklin O.M. Scott	ITT
Cotton	Acco Coker Delta Pineland	Anderson Clayton KWS AG Southwide Inc.
Hybrid Wheat	Pioneer Dekalb Cargill	

Sources: *Focus: Pioneer*, An investment review by Dain, Kalman and Quail, March 1974.
The Graham Centre, 1979.

in the seed industry than restrictive varietal legislation? In fact, since hybrids provide built-in 'patent' protection, might not governments' move to PBR be seen as an effort to stimulate non-hybrid plant breeding by equalizing the protection and the profit incentives? If this is so, then PBR might be regarded as a sound move, designed to safeguard genetic resources and protect the environment.

Between the theory that seed pelleting could reduce chemical use and the possibility that PBR could strengthen non-hybrid development, it is difficult to understand why 'patent' legislation has not become the cause célèbre of the environmental movement. The answer, of course, is because such arguments would irreparably strain public credibility. Farmers do not expect agrichemical firms to reduce the need for their products; and no one anticipates corporations will foresake the opportunity of forcing farmers back to the market every year, via hybrids, because of PBR.

There may be, however, a simple answer to explain the enthusiasm of the largest multinationals for this kind of legislation. With patent-equivalent protection, the long-term future of the industry seems sufficiently secure to attract investors. A variety can not, technically, be stolen by a rival firm; and royalty payments, for conventional non-hybrid varieties, can pay the costs of hybrid research. Only larger firms can afford the initial investment of time and advertising. Smaller firms will have to get out of the market. Thus, PBR becomes a means of reducing the number of competitors. For the multinationals, stringent patent criteria amount to nothing more than a helpful barrier blocking the innovative efforts of smaller enterprises.

PBR also brings another benefit. Once governments have paved the way for corporate investment by legislation, how can public breeding institutions continue to compete with the private sector offering the same crop varieties? Before long, the new seedsmen will cry foul and demand that unfair government competition be removed. Why, they can argue, should taxpayers pay to have public breeders do what companies are already doing? Why not have government work in areas not being pursued by private enterprise?

Variety control is the key; and, restrictive varietal legislation is the major tool. The restrictions come in two forms: government regulations controlling the quality of seed to be sold commercially (i.e. licensing regulations); and, 'patent' legislation enabling firms to organize the price and distribution of the varieties they produce. In the absence of patents and heavy corporate involvement, licensing mechanisms represent protection for farmers; but with PBR, licensing systems protect the corporations involved. The new seedsmen have changed the nature of the seed industry with: new reasons for plant breeding; a biochemical approach; and, increasing legal and administrative involvement. They will continue to do so, particularly as the legal issues become more prominent with the global spread of PBR legislation.

REFERENCES

1. From the covering letter accompanying the 'Prospectus' on *The Global Seed Study* circulated by L. Wm. Teweles & Company. Dated October 23, 1978.

2. Information provided by W.T. Bradnock in a January, 1978 telephone conversation.

3. Information provided by Cary Fowler in a November, 1977 speech to the Annual Fall Conference of the Saskatchewan Council for International Co-operation (Canada).

4. L. Wm. Teweles & Co., *The Global Seed Study*, 'Prospectus'. October 1978, p. 7.

5. "Seed Monopoly", *Elements*. February 1975, pp. 6-7.

6. L. Wm. Teweles & Co., op. cit., p. 2.

7. From a March, 1979 telephone interview with Jean-Pierre Berlan.

8. L. Wm. Teweles & Co., op. cit., p. 6.

9. Ibid., p. 6.

10. From INPADOC files. Patent is held by Kerr McGee Company.

11. From the covering letter accompanying the 'Prospectus' on *The Global Seed Study* circulated by L. Wm. Teweles & Company. Dated October 23, 1978.

12. *Focus: Pioneer*. An investment review by Dain, Kalman & Quail, March 1974, p. 1.

13. Salter, M.S. and Weinhold, W.A., "Diversification via Acquisition", *Harvard Business Review*, July-August 1978, p. 175.

14. From the covering letter accompanying the 'Prospectus' on *The Global Seed Study* circulated by L. Wm Teweles & Company. Dated October 23, 1978.

15. Ibid..

16. *Focus: Pioneer*. An investment review by Dain, Kalman & Quail, March 1974, p. 14.

17. Pioneer Hi-Bred 1977 Annual Report, p. 9.

18. "Seed Monopoly", *Elements*. February 1975, pp. 6-7.

19. *The Wall Street Journal*. October 4, 1978, p. 2.

20. *The Wall Street Journal*. October 3, 1978, p. 2.

21. Hill, P., "Rhone-Poulenc and PUK Sign Gardinier Agreement", *Chemical Age*. March 10, 1978, p. 2.

22. "The New Diversification Oil Game", *Business Week*. April 24, 1978, p. 76.

23. From the covering letter accompanying the 'Prospectus' on *The Global Seed Study* circulated by L. Wm. Teweles & Company. Dated October 23, 1978.

24. From a speech by Harris Gleckman of the UN Centre on Transnational Corporations at a symposium on plant breeders' rights in Regina, Canada on March 19, 1979.

25. *The Acquisitions of Technology from Multinational Corporations by Developing Countries*. UN ST/ESA/12, 1974, p. 45.

26. *Impact of Trademarks on the Development Process of Developing Countries*. UNCTAD, June 29, 1977, p. 21.

Restrictive Varietal Legislation

RESTRICTIVE VARIETAL LEGISLATION — PLANT BREEDERS' RIGHTS — WILL HAVE AN IMPACT ON THE AGRICULTURAL SECTOR . . . WHAT ARE THE IMPLICATIONS FOR THE VAVILOV CENTRES AND PUBLIC BREEDERS? WHAT ARE THE LEGAL IMPLICATIONS? WHAT BIASES AND EXPERIENCES WILL THE CORPORATE SECTOR BRING TO THE SEED INDUSTRY?

Chapter 7

The Implications of Restrictive Varietal Legislation

7.1 The Genetic Resources Link

I am with you on the importance of genetic diversity, and I believe that plant breeders' rights are restrictive and ultimately counter-productive.
— Sir Joseph Hutchinson, Oxford, UK, 1979.

Personally, as a geneticist and a 'gene banker', I am most worried about if UPOV and similar organizations work as institutions of law rather than of biology and agriculture. The view UPOV is now taking, demanding 'line purity' of self-fertilizing crops is certainly leading to genetic wipe-out; and in my opinion, also to less adaptable and more vulnerable varieties.
— Dr. Stig Blixt, 1979.

I do not believe that the issues of plant breeders' rights and plant genetic resources are unrelated. They are as much related as smoking and lung cancer. As cancer can occur without smoking, so can the depletion of genetic resources without plant breeders' rights in Canada. However, there is good reason to believe that the plant breeders' rights may promote and actually accelerate the genetic uniformity of crop varieties at a much faster rate than has been done so far by largely public plant breeding in the country.
— Dr. S. Jana, 1979.

In fact, the trend appears to be towards fewer and more uniform cultivars. (The recently enacted Variety Protection Act also tends to force cultivars towards phenotypic uniformity for accurate varietal description.) This may mean that breeders really do not believe in the dangers of genetic vulnerability; or it may mean that the pressures of the market place (the farmer and/or the processor) overcome the stated wishes of the plant breeder.
— Dr. D.N. Duvick, University of Saskatchewan, Canada, 1976.

Since the publication of our preliminary report, the issue of the potential link between genetic resources and plant breeders' rights has been hotly debated by agricultural scientists. Four Canadian professors at the University of Saskatchewan have gone so far as to argue: "Recognition that the depletion of genetic resources is in no way related to plant breeders' rights is a mandatory first step towards a reasonable and just debate of the pros and cons of the proposed legislation."[1] In the USA where patent legislation is less than a decade old, most regional gene bank directors see little connection between the legislation and their gene banks. People like Dr. Charles Adamson of Savannah, Georgia see PBR as making a positive contribution.[2] Others like Dr. Robert E. Hanneman Jr. of Madison, Wisconsin write: "Perhaps it deserves some limited attention."[3] On the European side of the Atlantic, gene bank directors and those scientists interested in genetics are largely unmoved by the possibility that PBR will contribute to erosion. Generally favouring PBR, Dr. Siguard Anderson nevertheless adds: "The administration of this law and regulations and the amount of scientific work spent on identification work is tremendous."[4] However, other conservationists and plant breeders detect quite specific dangers in the legislation:

The Uniformity Requirement

It is argued that the 'patent-like' demand for uniformity placed upon breeders in the USA and in Europe has led to increasing uniformity of crops. Even some individuals involved in the private sector, such as Duvick of Pioneer Hi-Bred and Blixt of the Weibullsholm Plant Breeding Institute, have expressed their concern regarding this issue.[5] According to Dr. N.L. Innes of the National Vegetable Research Station at Wellesbourne, UK: "Although for some vegetables there are as yet no plant variety rights, before seed of a variety can be sold that variety must be listed on the National List (or Common Catalogue) and is subjected to the same test as for plant variety rights." Innes goes on to say that varieties are lost in Europe because they are "too variable to be included in the National List."[6]

It is Sir Joseph Hutchinson, however, who makes the trend and the danger quite clear: "And this is where the plant breeders' rights legislation is so damaging. For administrative reasons, diversity will not be tolerated. If a man has a right to a reward for his variety, those who have to implement his right must be able to identify what is rightly his. So they insist that his variety must be so uniform that there can be no doubt about it. If this were as far as they were to go, it would not matter greatly. But they also insist that nothing must be grown except varieties that are equally identifiable. So you must not sell for seed anything except pure and certified varieties. Thus we are compelled by law to do our utmost to eliminate all variabilities from the most valuable stocks we have."[7]

The Hybrid Opportunity

PBR, or 'restrictive varietal legislation', stimulates corporate investment in plant breeding. Once stimulated, this kind of investment security inevitably leads to another kind of security in the form of hybrid breeding; which in turn has a direct impact on genetic resources. Taking the example of brussels sprouts, Dr. N.L. Innes notes: "It is not possible to gauge accurately to what extent the genetic base of sprouts has been narrowed by hybrid breeding, but personal contacts with commercial breeders in the UK and on the continent indicate that some breeding programmes have a very narrow base with inbreds derived from relatively few open-pollinated varieties." In the period since PBR came into being in the UK (1965 to 1974), open-pollinated varieties of brussels sprouts have dropped from 49 to 30, while hybrid varieties have risen from 1 to 41. Seventy percent of the acreage for brussels sprouts is in hybrids. Innes records: "Many old varieties have already been lost...increasing trends towards inbreds, hybrids and synthetics are leading to considerable genetic erosion."[8] With or without PBR, it is undeniably true that the profit motive would make corporate breeders favour hybrids. With patent protection and the royalty incentive, corporations tend to expand their breeding programmes to crops where hybridization is possible.

The Third World

Few developing countries — Argentina is a notable exception — have PBR legislation, but have offered 'special titles of protection'. Nevertheless, the legislative scramble in industrialized nations can, and ultimately will, affect the genetic resources of the Third World. In discussing the global implications of plant breeders' rights in the summer of 1978, Dr. Glen Anderson of the CIMMYT made reference to a number of 'rescue missions' carried out by CIMMYT staff in North Africa, where European-based seed multinationals were marketing inappropriate varieties to Third World governments in the region. Anderson also reported that bilateral and multilateral aid programmes from Europe to Africa often resulted in the distribution of inappropriate seeds, because European agricultural advisors promoted the best-advertised seed brands from home.[9]

At Wageningen, Dr. C. Dorsman considers PBR "most welcome" but adds: "The natural result has been a stream of better, highly bred varieties which replaced older ones not only in the developed but also in the under-developed countries."[10] According to Dr. Innes: "In the developing tropical world commercial and state seed companies are fast making inroads by supplying specialist seeds to growers, and now is the time to conserve as many land races and wild varieties as possible, both for the temperate and tropical regions of the world."[11] There is no doubt whatever that 'restrictive varietal legislation' contributes to genetic erosion in the Third World according to Dr. Erna Bennett. She sees the development of a protected base in the First World and the expansion to new markets in the Third World as only logical in corporate terms.[12]

*　　　*　　　*

In summary, the legal requirements of PBR encourage phenotypic uniformity which increases crop vulnerability and eliminates varieties. The European experience indicates that these eliminated varieties are often lost to humanity. Secondly, 'protection' provides the necessary profit security to encourage multinationals to move into the seed business. To maximize profit, these giant corporations direct their research dollars to hybrid development thus increasing crop uniformity and genetic vulnerability. Finally, to maximize the product life cycle and profit of new varieties, the industry markets its seeds in the Third World — increasing erosion in the Vavilov Centres and the danger of crop epidemics.

7.2   Public Versus Private Breeding

There is every reason to believe that future years will see a rapidly increasing demand for direct government involvement in the field of basic research. It is difficult to visualize how private seed companies will be able to cope with the growing financial burden created by necessary investments in long-term fundamental research.
— P.H. Nelson and A. Kuhn, KWS, F.D. Germany, 1973.

In addition, the survey indicated that the commercial companies recognize the importance of the kind of research being carried out by the experiment stations to the future of their own programmes and that more and more seed companies are actively supporting the quests for increased funding from state legislatures.
— Dr. Harold D. Loden, American Seed Trade Association, 1978.

Personally, I see research divided in the discovery phase, and the exploitation phase. I believe that much of the discovery work in plant breeding, such as genetic resistance to disease, that kind of discovery research will continue in the public institutions. Conversely, I believe that the exploitation of research can best be done by private enterprises.
— Byron Beeler, Ciba-Geigy, 1977.

During the 1960s USDA spent US $2.5 million a year for seed research in land grant universities. Seed companies would give the universities extra grants for hybrid research making hybrids particularly profitable for the universities ... By 1959 less than one dozen seed companies supplied the 12 million bushels of hybrid corn planted annually in the USA.
— Bettina Conn, 1975.

Faced with the possibility of PBR, some public breeders have enumerated a list of concerns which includes: a decline in government funding for public breeding; the involvement in the public sector of corporate breeders; a reduction in the free exchange of germ plasm within the scientific community; and, a deterioration of university training programmes for future plant breeders. The short history available on PBR in Europe and the United States makes it difficult to determine the real impact of the legislation upon public breeding. The UK experience appears to suggest that public breeding has not substantially suffered since legislation was introduced in 1964. The limited data gathered by the Canadian Government on the British experience shows that public varieties have held their own against corporate ones in that country; and that the public breeding programme has contributed to that government's foreign exchange earnings via overseas sales.[13] Conversely, the Dutch experience hints at extensive involvement in public breeding by the private sector.[14] In the United States, University of Nebraska researcher Don Hanway surveyed 47 state experimental stations in 1977, and found that 45 were still producing new crop varieties six years after the passage of the Plant Variety Protection Act: "...even though they have shifted emphasis more towards genetic programmes and population or germ plasm improvement."[15]

A 'Division of Labour'?

In industrialized countries, agricultural research is seldom, if ever, well funded. The flow of humanity towards larger cities and the preoccupation with industrial development make it difficult for plant scientists to compete with their more glamorous counterparts in industry. Finding it difficult to defend their research budgets, agricultural ministers sometimes turn to PBR legislation in the hopes of stimulating increased investment in the private sector. As Rollie Henkes notes: "Growth of private plant breeding might lull the public into the notion that it wouldn't hurt to cut back tax-supported programmes."[16] Some governments even spend their own money to stimulate private breeding.

In Canada, where the number of public plant breeders is on the decline and federal spending amounts to less than C $9 million a year, the National Research Council is making substantial cash contributions to corporate plant breeders. Interestingly, grants for corporate breeding began in 1967, less than one year after a federal agricultural committee concluded that there was no point in introducing PBR legislation in Canada because there was no private sector breeding.[17] The subsidized companies are now waiting for PBR legislation before bringing new varieties onto the market. It seems likely that the first 'home-grown' varieties to receive patent protection will be those the public has already paid for through taxes; and the farmers through taxes, then through royalties. At least two of Canada's most heavily subsidized companies — Stewart and Warwick Seeds — have already been bought out by multinational agrichemical companies.[18]

Table 14

Canada's National Research Council Grants for Plant Breeding (1967-1978)

Breeder	C $
Stewart Seeds (Ciba-Geigy)	$ 889,000
Maple Leaf Mills (Norris Family)	567,000
King Grain	261,000
W.G. Thompson	140,000
Warwick (Pfizer)	129,000
Otto Pick & Sons	95,000
Sask. Wheat Pool	52,000
TOTAL ('67-'78)	$ 2,133,000

Source: Finance Branch, National Research Council, 1978.

71

Table 15
Canadian Agricultural Research by Sector

Sector	C $
Research Branch	$106,000,000
Plant Breeders*	8,336,000
Economics Branch	2,000,000
Health of Animals Branch	4,000,000
Canadian Grain Commission	2,000,000
Departmental Library	2,000,000
TOTAL:	$116,000,000

* Within the Research Branch.

Source: *Orientation of Canadian Agriculture*, 1977.

Despite the adamant claims of Canada's Agriculture Minister, it would seem reasonable to anticipate some 'drift' in government resolve to support public breeding in the light of increased private breeding. Is this 'drift' really a disguised plot by corporate breeders to reduce competition? According to Rollie Henkes, both public and private breeders would welcome increased federal research in the United States.[19] This is so because, as Nelson and Kuhn of KWS and Beeler of Ciba-Geigy have made clear in public speeches, corporate breeders stand to benefit if the public sector continues to develop basic germ plasm while the private breeders 'exploit' the final cultivar in the market place. In other words, government agricultural research becomes a massive subsidy to corporate breeders.

A British government committee on 'Transactions in Seeds' conducted a crude survey of the seed industry in several European countries some years ago. The survey revealed the extent to which plant breeding in Europe is influenced by the private sector. In France, for example, the committee found most plant breeding to be in the hands of some very large companies. The committee assessed France's State Breeding Service as being "secondary to the private breeder in providing growers with improved new varieties." In the Federal Republic of Germany, most breeding of new varieties was entrusted to private breeders. Federal breeding stations were engaged in "fundamental work beyond the scope of most private breeders." State organizations also developed material "for issue to private breeders as a basis for further work." Despite this division of labour, state institutions were eligible for IPBR protection if they did produce new varieties. "The bulk of plant breeding is in private hands" in Holland, the committee reported. State breeding institutions "mainly do fundamental research work and...are not generally expected to carry their work forward to the point of producing new varieties." With a different approach, Sweden has given direct grants equal to 20% of the research budget of W. Weibull AB, Sweden's largest private breeder.[20]

A classic North American example of this situation is provided by the MH-1 tomato, developed by University of Florida plant breeders in close conjunction with the Florida tomato industry. The MH-1, derived from the

Walter variety, is particularly susceptible to ethelene gassing; i.e. allowing the tomato to ripen artificially but uniformly. In the Florida growing season of 1970-71, two University of Florida scientists discovered that at least 40% of the tomatoes shipped north were so immature that the seeds could be cut. In one shipment, 78% of the tomatoes were immature. As a result, US consumer groups have been highly critical of the public involvement in developing a variety which appears intended to trick the consumer into buying immature tomatoes.[21] However, the criticism should not rest with the public breeder. Confronted with limited research dollars and pressured into developing basic genetic material by the activities of private enterprise, public breeders are forced to develop material that is of interest to their corporate brethren. The task is to resist any 'division of labour' in the first place — and this can best be done by resisting PBR legislation.

Impact Upon Germ Plasm Exchange

Cautious in his criticisms of PBR, Dr. Norman Borlaug is nevertheless deeply concerned that restrictive varietal legislation is impairing the free exchange of germ plasm. Borlaug and Glen Anderson of the CIMMYT both refer to problems in exchanging genetic material with Europe and the United States.[22] Companies and government officials, on the other hand, argue that PBR will have little or no effect upon the free exchange of genetic material; and note that plant breeders are entitled to use the final cultivar for other breeding purposes. Plant patent holders can lay no claim to 'son of...' varieties.

These assertions fly in the face of the results of a March 1979 meeting of European scientists, brought together by the UNDP/FAO to discuss this very problem. The agricultural scientists divided germ plasm into five categories, and concluded that two of the five could be freely exchanged. Two other categories, it was agreed, could not be exchanged without some risk of commercial loss. The status of the fifth category was hotly debated among those present. In summary, the scientific community could not reach complete agreement on what might freely be exchanged, but they could demonstrate that PBR represent a serious restriction.[23]

A few months following the passage of the Plant Variety Protection Act in the United States, a *Wall Street Journal* article, "Seeds of Plenty", provided a run-down of corporate efforts to develop hybrid wheat; and a fascinating insight into the potential for corporate espionage. Cargill, one of the major hybrid wheat developers, draws blueprints of its test plots and locks them away in a safe. The plots themselves are unmarked as a precaution against robbery.[24] Despite the Canadian experience with Campbell Soup and Maple Leaf Mills (where the companies have not co-operated in germ plasm exchanges), Dr. Bryan Harvey of the University of Saskatchewan assured an audience in Regina that germ plasm exchanges would continue among "plant breeders who trust each other".[25] Commenting about this problem in 1976, Rollie Henkes reported that both public and private plant breeders in the United States were concerned.

That restrictive varietal legislation would restrict the free exchange of germ plasm should be a surprise to none. It is, after all, only logical. However, this logic was ignored by congressional leaders in the United States when it was raised — by then Secretary of Agriculture, Orville L. Freeman — in 1970: "If seeds and seed-producing plants had originally been included within the scope of the plant patent statues, a free and unhibited communication among breeders, both public and private, would not have been possible."[26] In his letter to Congress, Freeman strongly argued that restrictions to the exchange of germ plasm would have hindered the development of US agriculture.

The concerns of 1970 have not diminished. In a letter replying to protestations from the British Association of Plant Breeders that no connection exists between plant patent legislation and genetic erosion, Dr. O. Brauer, Director of the FAO's Plant Production and Protection Division replied on behalf of the Director-General: "As for the impact of plant varietal legislation on genetic resources, it is a fact that where such legislation is enforced, increased obstacles exist to the full and free exchange of germ plasm to which FAO and other UN agencies are dedicated. Plant varietal legislation is concerned with establishing proprietary rights over certain genetic resources and thus cannot but have a limiting effect on their availability." In the same letter, Brauer goes on to attribute genetic erosion to the Green Revolution and notes that conservation programmes tend only to be supported in emergencies. Risking the accusation that he is an alarmist, Brauer adds that the "FAO, as well as other agencies within the UN, are extremely concerned with the potentially disastrous situation arising from genetic erosion."[27]

*   *   *

The long term prognosis for public breeding is far from bright. Public breeding in the First World will undoubtedly continue well into the next century without significant monetary losses. As the years roll by, however, it will increasingly become a subsidy to corporate breeding or will be restricted to those crops of little or no commercial interest. Public and private researchers alike will suffer from the lack of a free exchange of genetic material. Third World governments and plant breeders — who provided the genetic material directly, or indirectly, in the first place — will be the last to receive, or to be able to afford, whatever genetic material remains to be traded.

7.3   The Regulatory Maze

It is the intention of the authorities to delete all non-traditional synonyms and some varieties from the list on 30 June 1980, after which it will be an offence punished by a fine of up to 400 pounds to sell them ... More than a thousand varieties will disappear.
— The Henry Doubleday Research Association, UK, 1979.

I am given to understand that the Common Catalogue will wipe out three-quarters of Europe's vegetable material within a decade after the regulations come into effect.
— Dr. Erna Bennett, Rome, 1978.

I would suggest that the entire licensing system that we now have should be abolished and we should start fresh.
— Peter Dyck, Canadian Seed Trade Assoc., 1977.

PBR is not the first piece of legislation relevant to the seed industry ever to be passed. Other regulatory agents, such as 'national lists' or 'licensing systems', have previously guarded seed quality control and the gateway to the market place. However, with the advent of PBR, changes in the over-all system are occurring. For example, national licensing systems are generally seen as protecting the farming community. Varieties licensed for sale are either 'as good as' or 'better than' other similar crop varieties. In a report prepared by Carl E. Buchting of KWS, the company notes that in Germany in the '30s "... 'so-called strange' or 'new varieties' had flooded the market, leaving the farmer prey to anyone that could do a good selling job. The forces of a 'free market' had created a situation, whereby everyone could sell anything as a new improved line of variety X or Y. Government legislation put an end to this nonsense."[28] Contrary to KWS's assertion, however, in the context of plant breeders' rights government licensing systems 'roll over' to become an important form of market control for seed companies with varietal rights.

In drafting PBR legislation for Canada, agricultural officials have underestimated the profound influence this legislation could have on Canada's licensing system. In the non-challenging, non-profit environment of public breeding, the licensing system works as it was designed to. In the highly profit-oriented environment of corporate breeding, the licensing system represents an opportunity to delete competitive traditional varieties and keep all but the biggest and strongest opponents out of the market. In effect, governments move to safeguard corporate market shares. For example, in an effort to standardize licensing practices throughout the Common Market, the Common Catalogue was created.

The Common Catalogue

However, Erna Bennett described the Common Catalogue regulations as "catastrophic" and "disastrous", and added: "Where there are now a hundred varieties of a certain vegetable, there may only be ten or twenty varieties 'legal' after 1981."[29] For further information Bennett referred us to Professor J.G. Hawkes of the University of Birmingham who admitted that the Common Catalogue "has some sinister side-lines for genetic resources preservation," but offered no connection between the catalogue and PBR legislation.[30] For further information Hawkes suggested Dr. J.K.A. Bleasedale of the Wellesbourne National Vegetable Research Station. Bleasedale described the Common Catalogue as a "self-inflicted wound" and interpreted the catalogue as a system of "legal" and "illegal" varieties heavily influenced by the patent problem of "proving" the individuality and ownership of varieties under UPOV. Faced with the loss of three-quarters of Europe's vegetable material within a decade, Bleasedale was asked why European plant breeders were not in an uproar. He responded that a certain "inevitability" prevailed and that "purely commercial interest dominates". In discussing the relationship between the Common Catalogue and UPOV, Bleasedale noted that "seed firms now sell a more restricted range of seeds."[31]

Lawrence Hill of the Henry Doubleday Research Association describes the implications for European farmers: "Here we have the enforcement of the law ... with the EEC regulations we are losing perhaps 400 varieties a year, but many more will go all over Europe ... Varieties which were once known under different names are now said to be the same; or, in official jargon, the one is the synonym of the other. Furthermore, varieties are being struck off the list every month as a 'maintainer' through his 'responsibility' for each variety decides that he no longer wishes to keep it. In August, for example, 126 varieties were removed including 'up-to-date', the onion with disease-resistance to downy mildew ... 32 varieties of broad beans 'got the chop' one June, 1978 ... the varieties which disappear most quickly from the list are the older types as growers join the mad scramble to produce more and more F-1 hybrids. This works to the detriment of the gardener, for plant breeders concentrate almost exclusively on producing varieties for food processors and aim for qualities such as colour, ability to hold water and thereby increase yield, simultaneous ripening for machine harvesting ... If you are looking for varieties with real taste, resistance to bolting, long harvesting periods, tender skins in the case of tomatoes for example, the choice is ever receding." With other angry gardeners, Hill lays the blame at the corporate doorstep: "Large seedsmen and commercial growers are chiefly responsible for maintaining varieties and don't seem to have any scruples when it comes to maintaining our vegetable heritage from disappearing."[32]

Concerned European governments have agreed to do all in their power to collect threatened germ plasm and have it stored at the Wellesbourne station. However, they have not agreed to pay for the preservation of the germ plasm — this apparently being slightly beyond their powers. The West German Government has put advertisements in their national newspapers, inviting concerned companies and backyard gardeners to send in their seed samples. We have yet to discover any other major national initiatives to equal Germany's efforts. However, Elizabeth Stamp (Oxfam-UK's information officer) confirmed that the Third World-oriented charity was considering funding the Wellesbourne centre because of the importance of Europe's vegetable germ plasm for developing countries. Stamp made it clear that

Oxfam's action was precipitated by the Common Catalogue and the failure of European governments to take adequate steps. She stressed that Oxfam was insisting upon the storage of some Third World-derived vegetable varieties as well as European germ plasm — although funds were not likely to be available for the rejuvenation of Third World seeds. In the summer of 1978, Oxfam circulated a budget proposal for funding consideration to the foreign aid officers of industrialized governments. Oxfam approached CIDA's NGO division in Canada, which may well provide the organization with more cash to safeguard Europe's genetic resources than Canada now spends on its own exploration and storage resources — or on support for Third World initiatives.[33]

In essence, the Common Catalogue leaves only the patented varieties on 'national lists' — although there are undoubtedly many exceptions — while eliminating considerable competition from traditional varieties. Genetic islands are virtually created around each patented variety to reduce ownership challenges in the courts. The 'illegal' varieties can neither be commercially sold nor grown (if they cross-pollinate) in proximity to a commercial 'legal' variety. The fine in the UK for doing so could be as high as £400. Sir Joseph Hutchinson sums up the absurdity of the situation: "But we have in recent years, particularly in Western Europe and in North America, done serious damage to our prospects of maintaining that diversity. In the interest of economic advance we have established varietal rights legislation, and in the EEC we are engaged in making sure that none but the most advanced varieties are allowed to be sold in the area, thereby very greatly restricting the diversity that is available to us. We are in fact selling our birth-right for a mess of pottage."[34]

Flexible Definitions

There are any number of ways to increase the corporate profit potential in the seed industry through changes in government regulations. A great deal can be accomplished through the ambiguities of plant terminology. For example, in the 1800s botanists identified over 100 distinct species of garden peppers. However, in 1898 it was agreed that only two varieties of garden peppers really existed. By 1923 the noted American botanist, Bailey, had determined that only one variety existed. Re-examining the situation following World War II, botanists reinstated many of the old, 'defunct' varieties.[35] Tomatoes also provide a classic example, in that the US Supreme Court of 1893 turned the tomato from a fruit into a vegetable so duty could be charged on Mexican imports.[36]

A lot can also be accomplished by redefining licensing standards. In fact, a relatively tough licensing system can be more beneficial to multinational enterprises, capable of meeting entrance requirements beyond the capacity of smaller firms. After all, crowded competitive markets require more advertising and research dollars than highly-controlled markets. One sure cause of tension for both public and private breeders is the co-operative testing process common to many countries. Even in the United States where there is no licensing system, troubles have arisen. Rollie Henkes reports: "However, some private seedsmen have questioned the impartiality of tests run by public institutions that have developed varieties that compete with the private entries. A corollary concern expressed by some public scientists is that some excellent public varieties may not fare well in the market place because they are not advertised as well as private varieties."[37] These are the tensions that lead to licensing changes.

The Third World's Position

The Third World is especially vulnerable from the legal angle. Companies, in fact, can claim patent 'rights' to varieties that are 'traditional' in developing countries; and hold these varieties either for their own marketing purposes or to keep the germ plasm out of the hands of competitors. For example, according to researcher David Barkin in Mexico City, one grain company obtained a certified variety from the Mexican Government and then patented it in Europe.[38] Barkin also reports that two major US seed outfits literally stole varieties from the CIMMYT breeding programme, had them multiplied across the border in Texas and then patented the material under the US Plant Variety Protection Act. For Europe and America this situation means exciting new plant varieties, but the Third World certainly does not benefit from this practice.

REFERENCES

1. Knott, D.R. et al., "Plant Breeders' Rights".

2. From a letter dated November 1, 1978.

3. From a letter dated November 6, 1978.

4. From a letter dated October 10, 1978.

5. a. Duvick, D.N., "Major United States Crops in 1976", in Day, P.R. ed., *The Genetic Basis of Epidemics in Agriculture*. New York Academy of Sciences, 1977, p. 94.

    b. From a letter from Dr. Stig Blixt dated January 22, 1979.

6. From a letter dated August 9, 1978.

7. From an undated letter received in early 1979 from Sir Joseph Hutchinson.

8. Innes, N.L., "Genetic Conservation and the Breeding of Field Vegetables for the United Kingdom", *Outlook on Agriculture*. Vol. 8 No. 5, 1975, p. 301.

9. From a telephone interview with Dr. Glen Anderson in June, 1978.

10. From a letter dated December 6, 1978.

11. From a letter dated August 9, 1978.

12. From informal responses to questions asked of a panel in which E. Bennett participated, at a symposium on plant breeders' rights in Regina, Canada on March 20, 1979.

13. From a speech made by W.T. Bradnock at a public debate on plant breeders' rights held in Swift Current, Saskatchewan, Canada on February 15, 1979.

14. *Plant Breeders' Rights*. Report of the Commission on Transactions in Seeds, UK, July 1960, pp. 20-1.

15. Loden, H.D., "Seed Industry Experience with Plant Variety Protection". From a speech made in California, USA. Circulated by the Canadian Seed Trade Association.

16. Henkes, R., "Growth in Private Plant Breeding Programs is Bound to Affect Public Programs ... and Farmers", *The Furrow*. May-June 1976.

17. From an interview with W.T. Bradnock in June, 1978 in Ottawa.

18. Information provided by the Foreign Investment Review Agency, Canada.

19. Henkes, R., op. cit..

20. *Plant Breeders' Rights*. Report of the Commission on Transactions in Seeds, UK, June 1960, pp. 18-24.

21. Whiteside, T., "Tomatoes", *The New Yorker*. January 24, 1977, p. 57.

22. From a series of telephone conversations with N. Borlaug and G. Anderson in June, 1978.

23. From a speech made by E. Bennett at a symposium on plant breeders' rights in Regina, Canada on March 19, 1979.

24. Brand, D., "Seeds of Plenty", *The Wall Street Journal*. September 8, 1971, p. 1.

25. From a speech made by B. Harvey at a symposium on plant breeders' rights in Regina, Canada on March 19, 1979.

26. From a letter to Congress dated February 29, 1968 from USDA Secretary, Orville Freeman.

27. From a letter from O. Brauer on behalf of the Director-General of the FAO dated April 17, 1979.

28. From information sent by C.E. Buchting of KWS to G. Eros of Oseco Ltd. in December, 1978.

29. From a telephone interview with E. Bennett on June 26, 1978.

30. From a telephone interview with J.G. Hawkes on June 26, 1978.

31. From a telephone interview with J.K.A. Bleasedale on June 26, 1978.

32. From material provided by the Henry Doubleday Research Association in January, 1979.

33. From a letter and draft project proposal from E. Stamp of Oxfam-UK dated July 18, 1978.

34. Hutchinson, J., Proceedings of a conference on 'Conservation in Agriculture' held in Oxford, UK, 1976. Panel comment.

35. Smith, P.G., "Garden Peppers", *California Agriculture*. September 1977, p. 11.

36. Whiteside, T., op. cit., p. 38.

37. Henkes, R., op. cit..

38. From correspondence dated January 10, 1979.

Chapter 8

Biases in Corporate Breeding

We're on the verge of something that's going to have a world-wide economic and nutritional impact...the Wilt Chamberlain of wheat.
—Byrd Curtis, Cargill, USA, 1971.

Between 450 and 500 new cultivars are licensed each year. Most represent minor genetic advances and 'fine-tuned' adjustments to changes in production, harvesting, processing and marketing procedures.
—*Conservation of Germ Plasm Resources: An Imperative,* US National Academy of Sciences, 1978.

And thus the original humble delicate fragile South American tomato has been transformed by American agricultural science into tough stuff — genetically manipulated and crossbred for high yield, engineered to resist the inroads of soil disease and the managing of certain machines alike, rendered responsive to a vast variety of pesticides, fungicides and artificial fertilizers, bred specifically for uniform maturing and destined for colouring in gas chambers, and provided with a hide to withstand endless shocks of shipping and repacking and the vicissitudes of supermarket display racks.
—Thomas Whiteside, "Tomatoes", *The New Yorker,* 1977.

In many situations, it is simply not feasible for a foreign seed company to risk an investment of its time, creative energy, germ plasm, financial resources and reputation in seed operations based on easy-to-save seed kinds such as rice, wheat, beans, sorghum and so on.
—Seed Industry Development, FAO, 1976.

It would seem a matter of simple mathematics that the stimulation of corporate involvement through PBR legislation would increase the number of plant breeders; and therefore, the number of varieties available to farmers. Such optimism is not entirely without substance. Government policy-makers must ask themselves, however, if the corporate breeders also possess biases counter-productive to the profitability of farmers and the nutritional requirements of society. Biases exist in all programmes. Public breeding programmes, quite naturally, are oriented to the greater profitability of the farmer. Public breeders balance the need for farmers to have a safe crop to grow at low cost, to the need for a crop to be marketable. Multinational agribusiness and agrichemical companies may be more oriented to the 'end product' profitability of the market place and less concerned with either the profitability of the farmer or the breeeding qualities which contribute to a secure harvest.

In examining the 'biases' of public and private breeders, we can see a number of potentially juxtaposed breeding orientations: the corporate breeders may be more interested in yield, uniformity, processing ability and appearance, while the public breeder may be more concerned with plant hardiness and disease-resistant characteristics; plant breeders from agrichemical companies may rely more heavily upon inputs of fertilizers and biocides, while public breeders may look for natural resistance through the multi-lining of crops; and, corporate breeders may be biased to crop improvement through hybridization which forces the farmer back to the company each year, while public breeders may look for crop improvement through the development of perennial varieties or appomictic hybrids (i.e. which allow farmers to save their seed). It would be wrong, however, to suggest that all virtue and scientific clarity rest with the public breeder. Rather, attention is being drawn to the natural 'biases' which occur when one group of scientists has no other objective than the profitability of farmers, while the other group of scientists combines this objective with the profitability of their companies.

8.1 The 'YUP' Bias

In an article, "Genetic Uniformity: The Growing Menace of Sameness", Ralph Reynolds reports: the malting industry in the United States tells farmers what barley to plant; the canneries determine varieties by contract; and each year eighty million acres of Californian tomatoes are bred to varieties primarily adapted to machine harvesting.[1] In August 1978, *The Wall Street Journal* reported that Maine farmers were either being forced out of business or into potato varieties risky to grow in their state. The 'Russett Burbank' — or 'Idaho baking potato' — is the preferred variety in the United States, because it is better for processing into french fries, potato chips and so on. According to the article: "The western shippers and processors can take over enormous quantities of potatoes, select the best-looking ones to be sold fresh and then process the off-size and off-graded ones."[2] This is the 'YUP' bias — breeding for 'yield, uniformity and processing' — which is geared towards the profitability of the company.

Potato growers in Canada's Atlantic region share the same fate; the pressure to grow what sells, not what grows. Were nutritional qualities at the heart of this matter, a challenging debate might arise between consumers and producers regarding their respective needs. As the 1972 report of the US National Academy of Sciences makes clear: "... survival of the fittest in this case has economic as well as biological meaning... vegetable processors ordinarily determine varieties to be planted on large acreages and insist on varieties tailored to suit their particular combination of requirements."[3]

Thomas Whiteside's incredible tale of the American tomato industry sums up the 'YUP' orientation taken to its extreme: "I telephoned Dr. William Hadden Jr., an auto safety expert who is President of the Insurance Institute for Highway Safety and asked him if one of his technical people could compute the approximate impact speed of the 'Florida MH-1' tomato in the six foot fall I had witnessed, in ratio to minimum federal requirements for impact resistance in the bumpers of cars sold in this country. Dr. Hadden obliged, and on the basis of tables that he provided, I concluded that Dr. Dryan's MH-1 was able to survive its fall to the floor at an impact speed of 13.4 miles per hour, more than two and a half times the speed at which federal auto bumper safety standards provide for the minimum safety of current model cars. This understandably represents a great step forward in tomato safety."[4]

Potatoes, again, offer a disturbing example of the YUP bias taken to its global absurdity. Despite the genetic poverty of Europe and North America in potato varieties, commercial imports of potatoes from the First World are replacing traditional South American cultivars in their centres of diversity. Although higher yielding, the imported varieties are nutritionally poor in comparison to local land races. Both Dr. D. Ugent and Dr. H.H. Iltis have noted that traditional potatoes offer an average protein content of 3.24% (determined by fresh weight and crude protein), and that First World varieties offer an average of 1.89%. While the highest yielding varieties of imports may reach the Latin American average under perfect conditions, many Andean and Mexican potato varieties have a crude protein level of up to 5.83%.[5] Traditional potatoes also have a substantially high percentage of vitamin C.[6] While the First World's YUP potatoes remain terribly vulnerable to disease, Ugent argues that Mexican varieties are hardier and that the "non-clean cultivation practices" of local farmers give native potatoes a considerable edge. The traditional varieties are also substantially more versatile in colour and taste, and therefore better able to meet the cultural requirements of the Latin American diet.[7]

It is worth pointing out that the potato also offers an example of the kind of options facing First World farmers with PBR legislation. Canadian agricultural authorities maintain that PBR is required in that country to allow farmers access to Holland's 'yellow-flesh' potatoes — which are so popular in world trade. Yet, as FAO officials note, Europeans developed new potato varieties from an exceedingly limited genetic base.[8] Rather than gain access to this terribly vulnerable European gene pool, Canadian farmers would be better advised to work with Latin American farmers to collect, and adapt, hardier and more nutritious Third World cultivars before they disappear. This would cost a great deal less and involve fewer risks.

The 'YUP' bias represents a threat to farmers and consumers alike: "It used to be that when you went to a country fair in the South, judges at the produce exhibits would come along, cut open the produce and taste it before handing out the ribbon... Now the ribbons go to whatever looks the biggest and the shiniest... scientists breed to increase the water content of tomatoes

... The tomatoes weigh more at the checkout counter so they cost more — but have you benefited nutritionally?"[9] When multinational agribusinesses such as General Foods (which recently bought out America's largest vegetable seed company, Burpee Seeds, and later sold it to ITT) move into plant breeding, this kind of 'bias' or research 'drift' may result. The YUP bias is yet more threatening in the Third World where Garrison Wilkes notes that the historic concern for "nutritional adequacy" among subsistent farmers can virtually disappear as First World agricultural systems seek chemically-induced high yields and the kind of uniformity that lends itself to machinery.[10]

8.2 The Hybrid Bias

As we have noted before, the royalties and market control available with PBR legislation attract giant multinationals, which ultimately invest the dollars necessary to develop hybrids in their chosen crops. Since some crops lend themselves to hybrid development and others do not, corporate breeders are under a powerful incentive to make the successful hybrids popular with producers and consumers. Thus, what is fundamentally a marketing consideration eventually influences the range of food varieties offered to people. Non-hybrid crops may lose land, and shelf space, to the hybrids.

On the plus side, hybrids can offer rapidly increased crop yield and a 'vigour' of real value to farmers. On the minus side, hybrids do not breed true to their lineage, and produce either useless or sterile seeds. Farmers are unable to save seed to grow another year and must return to the market place. The increased seed cost facing farmers is presumably offset by increased productivity. Dr. Richard Lewontin, the Harvard geneticist, questions the long-term merits of hybrids. According to Lewontin, hybrids increase genetic uniformity and displace the genetic variety in open-pollinated crops. Lewontin notes that four US companies dominate the corn seed trade. All four produce varieties that are virtually identical genetically, which are derived from lines produced at Missouri and Iowa State Institutions.

Dr. J.A. Browning of Iowa State University and Lewontin are both concerned that the genetic uniformity of US corn has not improved since the 1970 blight. In a paper due for publication in late 1979, Lewontin argues that the high yields achieved through hybrid corn development could now be achieved and superseded by yields from open-pollinated corn varieties. He maintains that at least 50% of the increased yield in hybrid corn is properly attributed to improved tillage practices; and the rest of the increase is achievable without hybrid development. Lewontin is convinced that a primary benefit in corn hybrids has been the market control gained by the seed companies. In other words, the short-term gains achieved by farmers are surpassed by the long-term market control achieved by the corporations. This results in increased genetic risk and higher prices for the farmer.[11]

Since the late '60s, Cargill, Funk (now Ciba-Geigy), Dekalb, Pioneer, Northrup-King (now Sandoz) and CPC International have been engaged in a bitter race to develop hybrid spring and winter wheats.[12] By 1974, Dekalb and Pioneer were marketing hybrid wheat to American farmers. Four percent of wheat planted that year was from hybrid seed. With over 100 million acres of wheat grown in the US each year, the market potential looked fantastic.[13] By 1976 it was reported: "At least 20 wheat hybrids are on the market this year, all of them from private firms."[14] Yet the hybrid wheats have not performed well. Western farmers who normally return to the market every four years for new seed and save their own seed the other years have not found the higher yields available through hybrids worth the price. Some companies, including Northrup-King, have even withdrawn from the hybrid competition. Plant breeders at the University of Saskatchewan have speculated that hybrid spring wheats will be impossible to develop; an opinion not shared by either Dekalb or Pioneer, who in recent annual reports were enthusiastic about future hybrid wheat developments. This conviction is also held by Dr. Glen Burton — a highly regarded US plant breeder — who recently told an international gathering of breeders in Iowa that hybrids would dominate the wheat seed market before the turn of the century.[15]

However, Burton likely has mixed feelings about his own prediction. From his Clifton, Georgia breeding station, Burton is working to develop appomictic hybrids — fellow scientists in India and Texas are also doing similar work in this field. This special quality is best known in 'Kentucky Blue Grass', but is also found in sorghum, millet, citrus fruits, wheat, corn and rice. Besides being inexpensive for farmers, appomictic hybrids are cheaper from the research standpoint and take substantially less time to bring to market. Regular hybrids take from four to ten years before being ready for commercial sales; appomictic hybrids might be ready for purchase within a year. Burton says if appomictic hybrids were to compete with regular hybrids on the commercial market: "I suspect the seed industry would not be pleased unless it bought the right to the seeds." An official at the USDA Plant Variety Protection office suggests that the development of an appomictic hybrid seed in a grain crop "could wipe out the seed industry". Dr. Duvick of Pioneer is not so emphatic: "If appomictic hybrids were developed so that they would be marketable, it would change the nature of the hybrid seed industry."[16]

This lack of enthusiasm by major seed companies is understandable. The FAO notes: "It is too easy for the cultivator to save his own seed or to acquire some by barter from a neighbour... In countries where hybrid seeds have been successfully introduced and where substantial emphasis is given to production of vegetables, a good opportunity for seed company participation does exist."[17]. It may well be that this quality in such crops as millet, sorghum, wheat and rice cannot be satisfactorily achieved. However, appomictic hybrids in crops such as millet or sorghum have the potential to make a major contribution to feeding the world's hungry at affordable prices. Major successes in this area may not occur until the next century, if at all, since multinational agrichemical companies — looking to world markets — see little to gain from this kind of research and development.

8.3   The Patent Bias

Appomictic hybrids represent one of several areas of innovative research presently being undertaken at government-funded research stations.

In Canada, a federal station is doing experimental work in perennial wheat. At the CIMMYT and Iowa State University exciting work is underway in developing multi-line cereals. With a multi-line, an otherwise uniform variety has built into it a number of slight genetic variations to improve its resistance to disease. Expensive and time-consuming to develop, a multi-line cereal could nevertheless be an important boon to crop yield for farmers fighting the never-ending battle against rust and fungi. J.A. Browning's multi-line oats are particularly good news for the rust-plagued Canadian prairies.

The problem with a multi-line is that it may not be patentable. The very fact of its genetic diversity may mean it would not qualify for PBR registration. KWS in West Germany has this to say: "The concept of multi-line varieties is by no means new; still, to our knowledge, varieties based on these principles are not available, plant breeders' rights or not. Multi-line varieties, if based on isogenic lines for stem rust resistance, say, will be phenotypically as uniform as any other variety."[18] In other words, it may be technically possible to patent a multi-line variety but no one is quite sure. A multi-line variety may be more exposed to patent challenges. After years of work, a multi-line may not pass the uniformity requirements established by PBR legislation. The legal interpretation of a multi-line may vary from country to country. These factors all tend to discourage extensive corporate investigation of what could be an extremely profitable area for producers.

8.4   The Chemical Bias

The opposite of multi-lining and other efforts to breed for disease resistance is to breed for the use of chemicals. This possibility has obviously occurred to the multinational agrichemical companies who are so actively buying into the seed industry today. Is it possible for a plant breeder to produce varieties which need certain chemicals? Many plant breeders think it unlikely. Breeding is difficult enough without throwing in a peculiar new requirement, according to Dr. B. Harvey at the University of Saskatchewan. Otherwise a supporter of PBR, J.S. Bubar of the Nova Scotia Agricultural College would disagree: "I share the concern that new varieties may only produce under certain restricted conditions, which may include use of certain chemicals."[19] With quite a different view of PBR, Dr. Lewontin of Harvard would support Bubar: "... there is legitimate reason to suspect that chemical companies will link chemical research to plant varieties they are developing."[20]

This academic dispute possibly stems from a misinterpretation of the ways in which chemicals and plant breeding may be linked. If you produce a short-stemmed rice so that the weeds about it are taller, you may need a herbicide to destroy the weeds. If you are a company that already has an effective herbicide for these weeds, you need only instruct your plant breeding department to breed for the short-stemmed characteristic. Since the short-stem variety may have many redeeming characteristics, the end result may be acceptable to farmers. The Florida 'MH-1' tomato provides a specific example. Amchem's 'ethrel' has long been used in the ripening process for tomatoes, allowing harvests to be 'scheduled' when appropriate. According to Whiteside, with industry encouragement University of Florida tomato breeders biased their breeding programmes to produce a tomato which would only ripen when sprayed. No doubt Amchem Products (now Union Carbide) will be forever grateful. However, consumers may be finicky about this kind of chemical connection, and industry is well aware of this. According to one processor: "We don't like to use the word 'gassing' where tomatoes are concerned...we like to refer to the process as 'de-greening'."[21]

There are many sound reasons for agrichemical corporations to involve themselves in the seed industry. In 1978, it was estimated that the cost of a new pesticide could run as high as US $15 million, whereas the cost of a new crop variety — including hybrid development — would cost only US $2 million.[22] Ciba-Geigy estimates the cost to be closer to US $10 million.[23] Delays in pesticide development are enormous, with each chemical requiring 65 toxicity tests at a cost of at least US $400,000. It takes eight to ten years to develop a new drug or pesticide, and as many as 5,000 chemicals may be synthesized in the process.[24] Given the high costs and the considerable danger that environmental agencies will withdraw the pesticide, agrichemical involvement in the seed industry represents a form of 'hedging' — i.e. a way of assuring that one product line needs the other.

*   *   *

Clearly, any breeding programme has its natural biases. Over-all, public breeders seem better able to balance the sometimes divergent needs of producers and consumers for the greater benefit of both. Corporate breeders, with their extensive involvement, are in danger of dividing their loyalties; in which case both producers and consumers may lose. In creating restrictive varietal legislation, governments should not naively assume they are leading the way to new and innovative forms of plant breeding or an increase in the over-all number of plant breeders. Rather, they are creating a new situation which does not appear to be 'officially' comprehended.

REFERENCES

1. Reynolds, R., "Genetic Uniformity: The Growing Menace of Sameness". Unknown newspaper article, p. 2.

2. Shao, M., "Small Maine Farmers Don't Get the Gravy with their Potatoes", *The Wall Street Journal.* August 25, 1978, p. 1.

3. *Genetic Vulnerability of Major Crops.* US National Academy of Sciences, 1972, p. 83.

4. Whiteside, T., "Tomatoes", *The New Yorker.* January 24, 1977, p. 61.

5. Oldfield, M.L., *The Utilization and Conservation of Genetic Resources: An Economic Analysis.* Master of Science Thesis, March 1977, p. 49.

6. Ibid., p. 57.

7. Ugent, D., "The Potato", *Science.* 1970, p. 1165.

8. From a letter from E. Bennett dated May 28, 1979.

9. From a speech given by Cary Fowler to Saskatchewan farmers in February, 1979.

10. Wilkes, G., "Native Crops and Wild Food Plants", *Ecologist.* Vol. 7 No. 8, p. 314.

11. From a telephone conversation on February 7, 1979.

12. Brand, D., "Seeds of Plenty", *The Wall Street Journal.* September 8, 1971, p. 1.

13. "Seed Monopoly", *Elements.* February 1975, pp. 6-7.

14. Henkes, R., "Growth in Private Plant Breeding Programs is Bound to Affect Public Programs . . . and Farmers", *The Furrow.* May-June 1976.

15. Information provided by D. R. Knott in a television interview in Saskatoon, Canada on March 27, 1979.

16. "New Seeds", *Elements.* June 1975, p. 7.

17. Feistritzer, W.P. ed., *Seed Industry Development: A Guide to Planning, Decision-Making and Operation of Seed Programmes and Projects.* FAO, 1976, p. 112.

18. From information sent by C. E. Buchting of KWS to G. Eros of Oseco Ltd. in December, 1978.

19. Bubar, J. S., From a drafted but unpublished 'Letter to the Editor' dated January 23, 1979. Circulated by the Canadian Seed Trade Association.

20. From a telephone conversation with R. Lewontin on February 7, 1979.

21. Whiteside, T., op. cit., p. 42.

22. Menninger, R., "New Crops", *The Co-Evolution Quarterly.* Fall 1977, p. 76. An interview with Richard Felger.

23. Waterloo, C., "Pesticides: What We Don't Know", *Des Moines Sunday Register.* April 23, 1978, p. 1.

24. Menninger, R., op. cit., p. 76.

Chapter 9

Learning From Corporate Experience

I do not know what is precisely meant by ammoniac manure. If it means guano, superphosphate or any other artificial product of that kind, we might as well ask the people of India to manure their soils with champagne.
— Lord Mayo, Viceroy of India, 1870.

In his quest for a buck, Gadsden is distressed that Merck's potential has been limited to sick people. He says he would love Merck to be like Wrigley's and 'sell to everyone'. Accordingly, it has long been his dream to produce some good 'healthy-people products'.
— Wyndham Robertson, *Fortune*, March, 1976.

It would be difficult to judge the seed industry by its past performance, because it is not the same industry as a generation ago — or even back in the sixties. It is possible, however, to consider the corporate performance of companies who are now involved in the seed industry; i.e. the pesticide and pharmaceutical enterprises. All three sectors — seeds, chemicals and drugs — place a heavy emphasis upon research. Drugs are often derived from plants; and plants are linked to agrichemicals. To some degree, the research work of a drug or chemical firm has long been linked to plant research. Unfortunately, R&D may have gone mostly into market analysis and product promotion. This syndrome appears to be rampant in pesticides and pharmaceuticals, and it might soon be so in the seed business.

9.1   Learning from the Agrichemical Experience

We have noted that the Green Revolution was also a fertilizer or agrichemical revolution; therefore, seeds and chemicals are already linked in farming practices. Now that biocide firms are also seed companies, however, there is more to understand about their interests in the seed industry:

Biocides

According to a report on Canada's biocide business, a federally-sponsored meeting of the Canada Weeds Committee complained about "the recent trend to an increased release of 'new' herbicides which are close chemical relatives of herbicides now on the market by the agrichemical industry."[1] This situation is by no means exclusive to Canada. Richard Felger of the USA comments: "With all the new pesticides, there are no fewer pests. The game is not being won, it is only being postponed."[2] The American market offers 63,000 biocides to farmers, backyard gardeners and householders, but few of these varieties are notably different 'chemically'.[3] Canadian crop losses, for example, have remained at about one-third of the total cereals crop ever since World War II.[4]

Corporate Concentration

There are only thirty significant agrichemical firms in the world. For the most part, they are also seed and drug companies. This corporate concentration is significant for smaller nations. If the local market is small , the local biocide companies are likely to be little more than sales offices for the major international firms. This is certainly true in the Canadian biocide industry, where firms largely import from parent enterprises. Furthermore, multinationals work for the biggest markets; smaller markets simply have to adapt to the broader research programmes as best they can.

Biocides in the Third World

Biocides are most needed in countries growing cotton, corn, rice, wheat, soybeans, deciduous fruits and nuts. As long as government subsidies are available, sales to the Third World are promising. Many companies are now marketing their biocides in developing countries. Their particular interest in the Third World has drawn the special concern of the World Health Organization, which claims that 500,000 of the world's poor become seriously ill each year due to pesticide sprayings. On many estates, 'dusters' fly over fields spraying peasant workers and crops simultaneously and without warning. The UNEP adds that over 300 insect species have mutated and are now not controllable by traditional chemicals.[5] In El Salvador, the incidences of malaria doubled in the early seventies despite constant sprayings.[6] If literacy problems do not initially prevent farmers from properly using agrichemicals, the actual costs of adequate protection might prove prohibitive.

The agrichemical industry has been described as one of the most poorly regulated in the world.[7] As a result of inadequate measures taken by the US Environmental Protection Agency, a number of unscrupulous chemical firms were able to export 77 million pounds of 'unregistered' or 'deregistered' biocides from the United States to the Third World in 1975. Although such exports are not illegal, the shipment of chemicals deemed dangerous in one country without warning to another country must, at least, be considered immoral. Between 1957 and 1972, the American foreign aid programme shipped US $550 million in biocides to the Third World. Although exact figures are not available, it has been estimated that a substantial portion of this total was made up in purchases of agrichemicals that had been 'deregistered' for the US market. In other words, with the help of the US Government, companies were 'dumping' dangerous goods on an unsuspecting market — the poor.[8]

Table 16
US 'Unregistered' and 'Deregistered' Biocide Exports to the Third World

Biocide	Patent Holder
Aldrin	Shell
Strobane	Tenneco
Toxaphene	Hercules
Heptachlor	Velsicol (sub. of Shell)
Lindane	Chevron Chemicals (sub. of Standard Oil of Cal.)
Endrin	Shell
BHC (Benzene Hexachloride)	Hooker Chemicals (sub. of Occidental Petroleum)
Methyl Parathion	Bayer & Monsanto
Parathion	Bayer & Monsanto
Dieldrin	Shell
Proxpur	Bayer & Chemagro
Leptophos	Velsicol (sub. of Shell)

Sources: Saskatchewan Department of Agriculture, 1978.
        Science, 1978.

Chemicals and Profitability

A clue to the lack of R&D creativity in the pesticide industry comes from Dr. Donald G. Manly of Air Products and Chemicals Incorporated: "We have an extremely strong profit centre oriented organization that strongly believes in the market pull rather than the technology push. R&D is viewed as an integral part of our profit centre organization. As a consequence of this, our R&D people tend to be more entrepreneurial in nature than the super-scientist type. In fact, in our college recruiting and our recruiting in general, we strongly bias our staff towards the non-scientific type of research work."[9] Manly might be expected to argue that the best road to profitability is through assuring the profitability of the farmer/customer. This simplistic answer has little appeal for peasant farm workers on Third World estates. The multinational firms who own the estates have defined profitability for themselves. It is the farm worker who becomes ill — not the company. Will agrichemical firms working in 'seeds' be any more concerned about the needs of the Third World, responsible in their export practices or innovative in their research?

A Noteworthy Connection

The advent of restrictive varietal legislation in any country will lead to an increase in products requiring testing. Whether the tests be limited to those showing uniqueness and uniformity, or whether they include tests for merit, public breeders are concerned that they will be left doing the work. Some Canadian breeders have identified this as a major shortcoming and opposed the legislation on the grounds that they would spend all their time testing corporate varieties. However, agrichemical experience offers another 'testing' option. Long-term drug and pesticide testing programmes in the USA are regularly turned over to private enterprise. The findings are spot-checked by government agencies but, by and large, the companies are trusted.

However, a few years ago, all this was changed by a company called Industrial Bio-Test Ltd. (IBT), a subsidiary of the chemical firm Nalco, which operates out of Chicago, USA. US government officials discovered that IBT — the leading 'tester' for drugs and biocides — had developed the bad habit of cheating on its tests. Rat tests, designed to last two years, were sometimes completed in 18 months by the simple expedient of manufacturing results for the final six months. Government investigators found serious faults dating back a full ten years. In total, 483 pesticides from 235 companies (involving 4,363 tests) were suspected of being improperly tested.[10] Among the major users of IBT, whose products had to be tested again, were some of the new 'seedsmen': Occidental Petroleum, Upjohn, Shell, Monsanto, FMC, Diamond Shamrock and Ciba-Geigy.

Among others, the Canadian Government has anticipated using the private sector for seed testing programmes. This could prove a serious error. Subsequent to the IBT discovery, US officials checked into testing programmes at 100 other private firms and universities. They discovered that most showed significant shortcomings in their testing procedures. One wonders whether there might also have been pressure from the companies whose products were being tested. Be that as it may, it is hard to believe that governments will be more careful in monitoring seed testing than they have generally been in monitoring drug and pesticide safety tests.

9.2   Learning from the Pharmaceutical Experience

Today's giant seed firms began their corporate lives in the drug industry. Even a cursory study of the history of the pharmaceutical industry makes clear that if these enterprises operate in a similar way in the seed sector, farmers and consumers will be in for some disturbing surprises:

Corporate Concentration

In 1974, *The Times* of London predicted that forty global drug companies would control 30% of an estimated US $50 billion in world sales by 1980.[11] Presently, three Swiss firms — Hoffeman-La Roche, Sandoz and Ciba-Geigy control about 15% of global sales. The latter two are also dominant in the seed industry.[12] Despite the tremendous variation in health problems world-wide, the pharmaceutical industry has found a niche for their drugs in most countries — and draw a large share of their annual sales from the Third World. In 1974, *Business Week* calculated that overseas sales for US firms would equal 40% of profits.[13] In that year, about one-third of all sales — mostly export — went to the Third World where governments spent US $2 billion on medicines. This bill has doubled in the past five years, according to Claire Brisset of *The Manchester Guardian,* and will amount to US $6 billion by 1981. Even in 1974, Third World indebtedness to the drug industry was US $1.5 billion — a very significant share of the total Third World technology debt.[14]

Restrictive Drug Legislation

Patents have played a key role in the pharmaceutical industry. However, as H. F. Dowling noted in a 1970 study of regulations related to the industry, the security that should come with patents has by no means led to increased innovation in research. Dowling offered the example of Parke-Davis's Chloramphenical drug that gave the firm large profits with 17 years of patent protection, but which led to no new medical innovations related to further development of the drug. This was in contrast to much greater research activity by other similar drug companies during that same period. The industry's complacency with profits and protection has extended to actual neglect of the plant genetic material which made the drugs possible. Once a natural source has been found and synthesized in laboratories, the tendency has been to allow field research and scanning to stagnate. The industry has become apathetic to genetic conservation even while recognizing the importance of plants to drug research.[15] According to *Business Week,* half of the best-selling 200 drugs on the American market will lose their patent protection in the early '80s.[16] Faced with a similar problem in the UK, the pharmaceutical industry had the choice of either undertaking aggressive R&D programmes or lobbying to extend patent protection. In 1977, the UK Patent Act was revised to give the industry four more years of security.[17]

Like the seed industry in many countries, the drug industry is subject to a licensing system guaranteeing some protection for consumers. Fisons describes what happened to licensing in the UK: "Section 31 of the 1949 Patent Act relating to compulsory licenses for pharmaceuticals was repealed following strong representations from the industry, but this benefit has been partly offset by the Licenses of Right Provisions of the new Act." The industry is now hard at work attempting to have the new licensing arrangements repealed.[18] Once again, one must wonder if the same companies will be as successful at adjusting legislation aimed at farmers as it is at changing legislation designed to protect people's health.

Advertising

Government and industry officials, speaking in defense of PBR, often argue that 'patent' protection will encourage firms to advertise their products, thereby educating farmers. Such an interpretation of the role of advertising is almost entertaining. However, some industry spokesmen would respond that advertising could be strictly controlled by government to assure farmers of factual performance data on the usefulness of every seed variety. The cost of such ads — although obviously part of the final cost of the seed — would be worthwhile, since farmers would be offered intelligent options relating to seeds; and incidentally, encouraged to use more certified seed.

There is a parallel here to the drug industry. Governments are deeply concerned that the public receive only clear and factual information on drugs. Indeed, most advertising is aimed at medical doctors whose years of practical experience should make them 'drug-wise'. Ad costs can run to as much as 15% of total drug sales, and often contain extensive and expensive drug performance reports. Unfortunately, we cannot assume that doctors always make wise choices in prescribing for patients: "One-third of all references (re: performance reports)...are from obscure journals funded entirely by the industry where manufacturers pay to have their papers published.[19] In a mid-seventies study prepared by The Haslemere Group in England, it was found that doctors were influenced by expensive ad gimmicks. It also reported that there was one drug representative for every eight practitioners.[20] Therefore, doctors have always tended to prescribe the more expensive brand name drugs rather than generic ones. *Business Week* reported that the American Government could save US $88 million a year if generic drugs were prescribed.[21]

Certainly, the new seed companies see advertising as an important means of reaching the farmer. Agricultural advertising on farm radio stations has increased in the United States at least 35% in recent years. Among the largest advertisers are Elanco (Eli Lilly), American Cyanamid, Ciba-Geigy and Monsanto. Not only does this advertising cost farmers money, it also reduces the competitiveness of publicly-developed varieties, since universities and governments are unlikely to compete aggressively with private companies for advertising space.[22] According to an American government official: "If a country is developing and does not have the educational system necessary for its farmers to read and understand the labels and information on varieties so that they can make a proper choice, this system will fail". The system he was describing was the 'truth-in-labelling' legislation used in the United States. Even in that country, there are over 1,000 buyer complaints each year.[23]

The classic story of seed advertising comes from a 1972 edition of *The Furrow*. As a hoax, the arrival of exciting new seeds was announced — including the 'super salad plant', 'pea-tatoes' and 'wheat beets'. The 'wheat beet' was wheat on top with sugar beets on the bottom so that you could harvest your wheat "while the beets grow on". The 'super salad plant' offered: "an outer layer of crisp green lettuce; next a tender ring of onion; then a colourful wrap of green pepper that encloses a superbly flavoured tomato." All farmers needed to do was add salad dressing. At last report, *The Furrow* was still receiving occasional requests for the seeds.[24]

If *The Furrow* can claim the classic story, *Canadian Business* can claim the classic advertising quote. Dr. George Jones, Director of plant breeding research for Ciba-Geigy in Canada is reported to have said that plant breeders' rights "would permit companies to advertise and sell anything the suckers (farmers) will buy."[25] Moreover, this is not a problem only the First World faces. For example, in an attempt to promote the Green Revolution, the Philippine Government gave a contract to J. Walter Thompson Company — possibly the world's largest dream merchant.[26]

Drug R&D

How creative and innovative have the seed giants been in their pharmaceutical research? Some feel that high-risk research in drugs should be done by government — echoing the view held by seed companies regarding government's role in plant breeding.[27] The drug industry's emphasis upon low-risk, commercially-viable pharmaceuticals has been well documented by the Sainsbury Commission in the United Kingdom. According to the commission, a 1965 study by a panel of British experts assessed the therapeutic effectiveness of 2,241 out of 3,000 products then available, and concluded that at least 35% were ineffective, obsolete or irrational combinations.[28] An American government study in 1971, which examined 2,000 products on their market, was still more critical; determining that 60% lacked evidence of their therapeutic claims.[29] Despite these findings, authorities in both countries have tended to allow the drugs to remain on the market. Speaking of drug R&D work in the USA, a former company research director told a Senate subcommittee in 1968: "The problem arises out of the fact that they (drug companies) market so many of their failures."[30] In fact, this vital industry has not offered the world the quality products it has the right to expect.

Pharmaceuticals in the Third World

Of the 69 new drugs approved in the USA between 1969 and 1973, 13 were first tested and sold outside the United States — largely in the Third World.[31] The trend was set by Dr. Gregory Pincus a quarter of a century ago, when he went to Puerto Pico to try out the female contraceptive pill on poor 'volunteers'. Since then, and for a variety of drugs, the Third World has amounted to a cheap testing ground for new products, representing a way of speeding up research by allowing tests on human guinea pigs.

Similarly, some Third World countries have represented an easy dumping ground for pharmaceuticals which were proven to be unsafe in the First World; or they have been a means of extending the product life cycle of obsolete drugs. Often Third World governments have been encouraged to buy drugs which serve no useful purpose. Five to eight hundred drugs from the First World would answer 80-85% of the medical needs of patients, yet the Federal Republic of Germany permits 24,000 drugs on the market and Italy allows 21,000. The World Health Organization has identified 200 key drugs for the Third World, plus a short list of thirty other complimentary drugs.[32] If drug companies have been willing to produce and market useless drugs in the Third World, might they not also breed and market useless seeds?

As we have already noted, the Third World has paid heavily for its pharmaceutical supplies. In the mid-seventies, the Sri Lankan Government offered clear evidence of gross overpayments for essential drugs, when that country opted to take control of the industry and to do its buying via tenders. For example, the Sri Lankan Government saved itself over US $140,000 in foreign exchange in 1975 — in four drugs — by forcing the industry to compete. Although many companies were involved, drugs have been selected for the table which were offered by traditional suppliers who are also seed companies — Sandoz and Ciba-Geigy.[33]

Table 17

Savings Incurred by the Sri Lankan Government in Selected Pharmaceutical Products through Tendering

Traditional Drug Supplier:	Pharmaceutical Product:	A. Traditional Supplier's Price	B. Successful Supplier's Price	'B' as % of 'A'
		US $ 1975		
Ciba-Geigy	Phenylbutazone	107,493	17,828	17%
	Imipramine	20,932	2,846	14%
	Clioquinol/Hydro-cort Cream	48,889	18,763	38%
Sandoz	Oxytocin Inj.	4,257	688	16%
		US $ 1974		
Ciba-Geigy	Nikethamide Inj.	1,292	181	14%
	Liethandienone	29,121	4,216	15%
	Tetracosactrin Inj.	11,636	9,867	85%
Sandoz	Belladonna-C Phenobarb	11,046	934	8%
	Belladonna & Ergot	1,383	650	47%
	Lanatocide-C	2,954	724	25%

Source: *Cases Studies in Transfer of Technology: Pharmaceutical Policies in Sri Lanka,* Study of the UNCTAD Secretariat TD/B/C.6/21, 1977.

Sri Lanka's experience has encouraged forty-three Third World countries to launch their own pharmaceutical programmes. Initiatives range from the creation of a single national purchasing agency for essential drugs to all-out efforts to establish an independent national industry. Sadly, this movement towards national self-reliance in drugs may occur in countries which are simultaneously turning over plant breeding to the same companies they have examined and found wanting in the pharmaceutical sector. It is hardly surprising that Fisons was moved to note in its annual report that there exists a "hostile attitude of governments throughout the world towards the pharmaceutical industry."[34] Indeed, several pharmaceutical/seed companies, such as Pfizer and Upjohn, are currently in the courts fighting lawsuits — in their cases from India and Colombia.[35] Ciba-Geigy has also recently been the target of a massive class action lawsuit for its marketing of 'Clioquinol' in Asia. Japanese officials estimate that 10,000 patients in that country have suffered serious side effects from the drug. Non-government sources place the figure at closer to 30,000. Victims claim that the company knew about the drug's shortcomings but continued to market it without appropriate warnings. Ciba-Geigy has agreed to an out-of-court settlement.[36]

Table 18
Seed Enterprises Reporting Questionable Foreign Payments to the US Securities and Exchange Commission

Company	Aggregate Questionable Foreign Payments	% Foreign Sales 1975
Anderson Clayton	US$ 2,160,000	—
Celanese	Not Material	25
ITT	11,338,000	52
Monsanto	3,624,700	29
Pfizer	1,665,458	57
Purex	447,336	—
Rohr-Amchem*	272,090	21
Upjohn	890,771	39

*Rohr-Amchem sold off its Amchem Products subsidiary in early 1977 to Union Carbide. Both Union Carbide and Amchem Products are involved in plant breeding.

Source: The Council on Economic Priorities, New York, 1977.

The global pharmaceutical industry has been distrusted in the Third World, not only for its high prices and its abuse of the patent system, but also for its extensive use of restrictive business practices. One such practice came to light in 1975 with pressure from the US Securities and Exchange Commission (SEC). Companies were given a grace period in which to declare 'questionable overseas payments' — more commonly known as 'bribes' — made to people in other countries. The pharmaceutical industry ranked second only to the aerospace industry in the USA for the extent and amount of such dubious payments. Although not all payments went to the Third World, industry analysts reported that almost all did end up in developing countries. Moreover, the firms included were seed, as well as drug, enterprises.

REFERENCES

1. Saidak, W.J., "Weed Science Research", *The Agrologist.* Summer 1977, p. 17.

2. Menninger, R., "New Crops", *The Co-Evolution Quarterly.* Fall 1977, p. 76. An interview with Richard Felger.

3. Waterloo, C., "Pesticides: What We Don't Know", *Des Moines Sunday Register.* April 23, 1978, p. 1.

4. "Agriculture to the Year 2000", Draft Report. Science Council of Canada, 1977, p. 71.

5. "Half Million Poisonings Blamed on Third World Pesticides Use", *The Western Producer.* March 23, 1978, p. 37.

6. Ibid., p. 37.

7. Ibid., p. 37.

8. Ibid., p. 37.

9. Manly, D.G., "The Dual Ladder — Successes and Failures", *Research Management.* July 1977, p. 31.

10. Lublin, J.S., "A Lab's Troubles Raise Doubts about Quality of Drug Tests in US", *The Wall Street Journal.* February 21, 1978, p. 1.

11. The Haslemere Group, *Who Needs the Drug Companies.* The Haslemere Group, War on Want and Third World First publication, Undated, p. 4.

12. Ibid., p. 4.

13. "The Drug Industry's Clouded Future", *Business Week.* November 23, 1974, p. 64.

14. Brisset, C., "Third World Medicines: Multinationals Rule", *The Manchester Guardian.* January 21, 1979, p. 13.

15. Dowling, H. F., *Medicines for Man: The Development, Regulation and Use of Prescription Drugs.* Knopf Publishing, 1970, p. 108.

16. "The Drug Industry's Clouded Future", *Business Week.* November 23, 1974, p. 65.

17. Fisons 1977 Annual Report. p. 11.

18. Ibid., p. 11.

19. Ibid., p. 11.

20. The Haslemere Group, op. cit., p. 25.

21. "The Drug Industry's Clouded Future", *Business Week.* November 23, 1974, p. 65.

22. Henkes, R., "Growth in Private Plant Breeding Programs is Bound to Affect Public Progams...and Farmer's", *The Furrow.* May-June 1976.

23. Rollin, S. F. (USDA), "Recent Organizational Developments and Future Trends in Variety and Seed Control — Truthful Labeling Concept", *The Role of Seed Science Technology in Agricultural Development.* FAO, 1973, p. 231.

24. The story was told by Cary Fowler of the Graham Centre in the USA.

25. Romahn, J., "Seeds of Discontent", *Canadian Business.* February 1979, p. 88.

26. Perelman, M., *Farming for Profit in a Hungry World.* Landmark Series, 1977, p. 158.

27. *The Manchester Guardian,* November 20, 1974, p. 14.

28. The Haslemere Group, op. cit., p. 12.

29. Ibid., p. 13.

30. Ibid., p. 13.

31. "The Drug Industry's Clouded Future", *Business Week.* November 23, 1974, p. 67.

32. *The Selection of Essential Drugs.* World Health Organization, 1977.

33. *Case Studies in Transfer of Technology: Pharmaceutical Policies in Sri Lanka.* Study of the UNCTAD Secretariat, TD/B/C.6/21, 1977.

34. Fisons 1977 Annual Report. p. 11.

35. "How Anyone Can Join the Great American Anti-Trust Game", *The Economist.* January 21, 1978, p. 85.

36. "SMON: The Human Cost of Drug Industry Profits", *Ampo.* The Japan-Asia Quarterly, Vol. 10 Nos. 1 and 2, 1978, p. 76.

Summary

The Issues

Some Third World farmers are opting out of the Green Revolution and returning to traditional crop varieties, because the so-called greening of the Third World is not working for the poor of many countries. Moreover, the Green Revolution is only the most visible part of a much larger agricultural revolution involving farmers and consumers everywhere — the 'Seed Revolution'. This revolution is guided by a relatively small number of multinational agrichemical/pharmaceutical enterprises who are now moving rapidly into the seed industry. Because seed is so pivotal to the entire food system, the intervention of these international firms and their natural bias towards chemical inputs is of profound importance to the future food security of the world. The 'Seed Revolution' is being aided by two key trends: the move in the Third World towards a second phase of the Green Revolution, which will leave plant breeding to the multinationals; and, an attempt in the First World to create patent-equivalent protection and market control of seeds for the same multinational interests. Both trends are heavily influenced by private enterprise.

Much more needs to be known about the 'Seed Revolution'. The pace of change is rapid and difficult to analyze. Right now, national governments are making policy decisions related to a revolution which they have not planned and do not really perceive. The following is a summary of our findings, offered as a basis for further discussion and study:

a. The world looks to a handful of plants for its survival. Be it wheat, maize or rice, each of the earth's major crops has its genetic home in the Vavilov Centres of genetic diversity, located in the Third World. Although everyone draws from the germ plasm in these areas to maintain food supplies, the gene-hungry nations of the First World are especially dependent upon the Third World for their crop survival;

b. The mythology of the 'population explosion' has led to the spread of 'high-response' plant varieties via the Green Revolution. New varieties are replacing traditional cultivars and wild relatives in the centres of genetic diversity, wiping out sources for future plant breeding and leaving traditional farmers wholly dependent upon expensive new varieties;

c. Global companies have virtual control over the second phase of the Green Revolution, allowing them to 'package' inputs of seeds and chemicals with the help of government subsidies, foreign aid and higher farm prices;

d. As a result, agrichemical firms have constructed a global distribution system and marketing strategy for their seed and chemical products, at the same time as competition from traditional crop varieties has been reduced;

e. There is a widely-held illusion that vanishing germ plasm is being safely stored in regional and global gene banks. In fact, these banks are poorly funded and have experienced disastrous equipment failures resulting in the loss of precious genetic resources. More collections are urgently required in almost every part of the world;

f. The emerging network of gene banks takes national genetic treasures from the Third World to be stored abroad. In effect, these national resources cross a technological frontier, robbing the world's original plant breeders — subsistent farmers — of their rightful heritage, and leaving Third World governments dependent upon the First World for access to their own germ plasm. In Africa, examples already exist where nations have paid to import the immediate genetic offspring of their national resources;

g. An unknown factor in genetic conservation programmes is the extent of corporate collections. It is known that in some crops a single enterprise dominates total world germ plasm holdings;

h. Protected by restrictive varietal legislation (patents), agrichemical/ pharmaceutical firms in the First World are moving aggressively to achieve variety control in major markets. Smaller seed companies are quickly disappearing. Public sector plant breeding is being virtually forced into doing basic research in areas of interest to the dominant companies;

i. Agrichemical corporations seek the development of plant varieties best able to stimulate chemical sales. The resulting bias can lead to greater crop uniformity and disease vulnerability as well as increased financial and environmental costs. The largest enterprises have created genetic research centres, cross referencing plant, animal and human chemical research;

j. Because of their involvement in several phases of the total food system, agribusiness plant breeders look to profits from several sectors. This enables them to breed seed suitable to their chemical, processing or retail interests, but not necessarily suitable to the profitability of the farmer or the nutrition of the consumer.

Conclusions

The 'Seed Revolution' has been discovered — and is being debated — at a time when it can still be halted and turned around. The financial resources and technicial expertise required to collect and conserve endangered germ plasm is well within the political reach of governments and agencies. Knowledgeable governments can act to protect public breeding programmes and curtail the expansion of the global seed industry into their own territory.

The key to mobilizing the political 'will' required to protect the world's genetic base lies in understanding some major myths:

a. the myth that the 'population explosion' threatens our food resources and makes necessary the kind of draconian development strategies evidenced by the Green Revolution;

b. the myth that the First World has the answer to increased food security through high energy-input production technologies; and,

c. the myth that agrichemical companies will bring innovation and creativity to plant breeding rather than uniformity and chemical dependence.

The creativity and genius of agriculture continues to lie where it has always been — with farming families. We do not propose a retreat to old technologies or a withdrawal of scientific expertise, but we do affirm that the long-term security of a global food supply and the basis for plant breeding programmes must rest with the viability of subsistent farmers to maintain their rural life. These families will protect our plant genetic resources better than gene banks and data centres.

This document does not so much arrive at a 'watershed' time when the crisis has reached a peak, as a time when the myths can be more clearly revealed. The very nature of plant breeding and the pace of government legislation will undoubtedly spread the crisis over decades. We are in the midst of the 'revolution'. We can still stop it and develop a way to achieve increased crop genetic diversity and greater public involvement in conservation and breeding. It is not too late. However, whereas it has taken humanity ten thousand years to bring our food supply to its present state, we could do irreparable damage within the next decade.

Recommendations

The 'Seed Revolution' is far from complete. We are hopeful that policy-makers and farmers world-wide will examine the implications of the changes now underway and take steps to avert irreparable damage to global food supplies. The almost complete interdependence of First and Third World germ plasm requirements leads one to hope that international co-operation can guarantee the Third World control over its own plant genetic heritage, while allowing the First World fair access to needed plant material. To this end, we offer a number of recommendations:

A. Regarding Germ Plasm Conservation

1. We recommend that a global germ plasm collection campaign be launched through the auspices of the International Board for Plant Genetic Resources, directed to the collection of both land races and wild species. Such a campaign should begin immediately and should be well funded.
2. We recommend that collected genetic material be stored in the country where it is collected in long-term storage vaults, where it can be adequately documented and rejuvenated as appropriate. We also recommend that staff be trained within each country so that they will be able to collect, conserve and document plant material;
3. We recommend that a system of genetic reserves be created in each of the Vavilov Centres where, as far as is practicable, native vegetation may be allowed to flourish;
4. Recognizing the costs involved in such a conservation programme, we recommend that mutilateral arrangements be made through the IBPGR to create an annual emergency budget of US $100 million for the collection of material, its storage in national gene banks, the creation of national and international botanical reserves, and the training of national staffs;

B. Regarding International Legal Arrangements

1. We recommend that the United Nations — through such organizations as the UNDP, FAO, and World Intellectual Properties Organization —

take appropriate steps to ensure that plants be regarded as resources of common heritage to all peoples and unsuitable for any form of exclusive control through patents, trademarks, etc. — i.e. that access to plant material be considered a basic human right;

2. We recommend that the 'Code of Conduct for Transnational Corporations' specifically include provision that the seed industry be regarded as an area of vital national security, inappropriate for the involvement of international firms;

3. We recommend that the 'Code of Conduct for the Transfer of Technology' include provisions guaranteeing the right of nations to protect their national botanical heritage from commercial exploitation;

C. Regarding International Action

1. We recommend that 'Seeds' become an agenda item at upcoming UN conferences dealing with international trade, agricultural development, and international scientific and technologial exchanges;

2. We recommend that the United Nations incorporate concern for this, issue in its 'Programme of Action for the Third Development Decade', and that one year of this decade be declared International Seed Year in order to launch a global conservation campaign;

3. We recommend that the UN Centre of Transnational Corporations undertake a special study of the world seed industry with its pharmaceutical/agrichemical connections, with special regard to its influence on restrictive varietal legislation and the control of genetic resources;

D. Regarding Third World Options

1. We recommend that those Third World nations who have not already done so take immediate inventory of their endangered plant genetic resources and plant breeding programmes to ensure that their sovereignty over this vital area is well protected;

2. We recommend that Third World governments press for a major programme of international co-operation to collect and preserve the world's valuable genetic resources;

3. We recommend that Third World governments closely monitor the spread of restrictive varietal legislation in industrialized countries to safeguard against any threat this trend imposes upon national conservation and breeding programmes;

4. In safeguarding its plant resources and food supply for future generations, we recommend that the Third World be aware of its own position in maintaining long-term world food security, and that it use its influence to promote international co-operation in conservation programmes;

E. Regarding the Role of Voluntary Agencies

1. We recommend that voluntary agencies examine their own potential for supporting collection, storage and training programmes in the Third World. Although co-operation with governments is important, we particularly commend programmes in support of the collective self-reliance of subsistent farmers already struggling to safeguard traditional plant material;
2. We recommend that voluntary agencies examine the public breeding programme and varietal legislation in their home countries to be assured that national programmes are operating with due regard to long-term food security and are not threatening the genetic resources of the Third World. We commend the initiative of Oxfam in the United Kingdom in moving to safeguard the world's vegetable germ plasm resources. We likewise commend the Canadian Council for International Co-operation for moving to oppose Plant Breeders' Rights legislation in that country;

F. Regarding the Personal Response of the Individual

1. On a personal basis and through organizations of which you are a member, you can support conservation programmes and oppose restrictive legislation;
2. You can also make a direct contribution to genetic conservation by planting your own garden with non-hybrid varieties and by saving your seeds for future gardens. You can also share your seeds with other gardeners and set aside some space for the growing of traditional, endangered seeds. For further information on how to do this, and where to go to obtain traditional seeds, write to "The Seeds Directory", The Graham Centre, Route 3, Box 95, Wadesboro, North Carolina 28170, USA.

Appendix A

Corporate Profiles

The following alphabetical survey of major firms involved in the seed industry — derived from industry sources* — should not be considered a complete listing. Companies selected are those most active in North America, or those who have been specifically referred to in this document.

ANDERSON CLAYTON—USA (1977)

Sales: US $947,953,000
US Fortune Rank: #252
Employees: 12,757
Product Lines: Oilseed Processing — Animal and Poultry Feeds — Planting Seed — Coffee Merchandising — Consumer and Institutional Food Products.
Seed Activities: Anderson Clayton sells seed corn in 15 states — also sorghum and cotton seed. Company faces a class action suit in Indiana related to the 1970 southern US corn leaf blight. Feed and seed operations amount to 7.5% of total sales. Recently, the company purchased two seed enterprises: Paymaster Farms and Tomaco-Genetic Giant.
Other: Company also has a US $550 million international food business with non-consolidated subsidiaries in Mexico and Brazil. Well-known brands include Chiffon Margarine and Seven Seas Salad Dressing. Anderson Clayton has admitted to US $2,160,000 in questionable foreign payments.

CARGILL—USA (1976)

Sales: US $10 billion
Forbes Private Sector Rank: #1
Product Lines: Cargill is actively involved in grains commodity trading, salt, cement, oilseeds, seeds, transportation, etc. If ranked on the Fortune list, it may have ranked as the 12th largest industrial enterprise in the USA in 1976. The firm is thought to be the world's largest in the grain trade.

---

*Annual Reports, the Foreign Investment Review Agency, *The Wall Street Journal* and *The Financial Post*.

Seed Activities: Cargill bought Dorman Seeds in the USA and Kroecker Seeds in Canada. The firm is active in hybrid wheat breeding.
Other: The company has been implicated in a number of legal actions related to grain buying and exporting in North America, Panama, and Europe.

CELANESE—USA (1977)

Sales: US $2,320,000,000
US Fortune Rank: #106
Employees: 32,100
Product Lines: Fibers — Chemicals — Plastics — Polymer Specialities.
Seed Activities: Company has recently purchased Cepril Inc. and Moran Seeds. Under its R&D diversification programme, the company is particularly looking at agricultural products — especially polymeric coating systems for field, forage and vegetable seeds.
Other: The firm is actively involved in guar gums, originating from India and Pakistan, and used in paper-making. Celanese has plants in 15 countries and sales operations in 70 countries. Celanese is recorded by the US SEC (Securities and Exchange Commission) as having admitted to questionable foreign payments. Celanese provides intermediate chemicals for the pharmaceutical industry.

CENTRAL SOYA—USA (1977)

Sales: US $2,177,385,000
US Fortune Rank: #115
Employees: 9,500
Product Lines: Grain — Refined Oils — Poultry — Food — Feed — Soybean Processing. Company has sales in over 70 countries.
Seed Activities: O's Gold Seed Company is a recent purchase and moves Central Soya into the hybrid corn seed market — also alfalfa and sorghum.
Other: Company feeds division has extensive plant operations in Brazil, Puerto Rico, Trinidad, Jamaica, Portugal, Holland and Canada. Central Soya also exports feed and animal health care products to the Far East, Middle East and Eastern Europe. Under Master Mix and Farmacy brand names, firm markets insect control, animal health care and feed products. In 1977, the company agreed to pay US $2.1 million in damages related to a US anti-trust action involving the production, processing and marketing of broiler chickens.

CIBA-GEIGY LTD.—Swiss (1977)

Sales: US $4,151,660,000
Intern'l Fortune Rank: #52
Employees: 74,080
Product Lines: Dyestuffs and Chemicals — Pharmaceuticals — Agrichemicals — Plastics and Additives. Primarily a pharmaceutical enterprise, the company has manufacturing facilities in 52 countries; 54% of total sales are outside of Europe with at least 28% of total sales occurring in the Third World.

110

Seed Activities: In North America, the company has recently bought Funk Seeds Intern'l and Stewart Seeds (Canada). The company has expanded plant breeding programmes in Canada, Argentina and Brazil. Major US seed sales are for corn and sorghum. World-wide seed sales in 1977 equalled Sw. Fr. 241 million.

Other: Company owns Green Cross agrichemicals firm. Recent plant protection products include Dual (herbicide) and Curacron (insecticide). Agrichemical sales in 1977 were worth Sw. Fr. 2469 million. Plant protection amounted to Sw. Fr. 1972 million of this figure. Markets for biocides include India, Mexico, Brazil, Argentina and South Africa. Ciba-Geigy has achieved some notoriety in Japan for its involvement in the 'SMON' case, where many Japanese became seriously ill (and some died) from taking its anti-diarrhea drug. The company is making massive payments to families and patients. Ciba-Geigy also had 13 of its major new pesticides retested in the USA following discovery of negligence by a private testing firm — Industrial Bio-Test Ltd. (IBT) There is also concern that its biocide, Atrazine, used on corn may cause mutations in the crop. Along with other major Swiss firms, Ciba-Geigy has been named by the Berne Declaration Group in Switzerland for its active involvement in influencing the 'Group of Eminent Persons', created by the UN to examine the role of multinational corporations in developing countries.

DEKALB AGRESEARCH INC.—USA (1976)

Sales: US $360,864,000
Employees: 18,000
Product Lines: Hybrid Seed — Poultry Layers and Swine Breeding Stock — Livestock Marketing and Commodity Trading Services — Irrigation Systems — Oil and Gas Development. Lindsay irrigation equipment is marketed in South America, Australia and the Middle East, as well as North America. Company also has fertilizer and agrichemical operations through Arizona Feed.

Seed Activities: Dekalb is particularly active in hybrid corn and sorghum as well as alfalfa and legume-grass forage mixtures. Dekalb is active in breeding and in sales in — among other countries — Mexico, Nicaragua, Brazil, Argentina, Italy and Canada. The company is dominant in the USA in hybrid wheat and corn.

Other: It is understood that the company is involved in litigation related to the southern US corn leaf blight of 1970.

DIAMOND SHAMROCK—USA (1977)

Sales: US $1,530,382,000
US Fortune Rank: #166
Employees: 11,279
Product Lines: Diamond Shamrock is involved in oil, gas, salt, food ingredients, animal antibiotics, feed supplements, fungicides, herbicides and seeds.

Seed Activities: Firm recently purchased Taylor-Evans Seed Company.

Other: Fungicides are directed to tomatoes, potatoes and groundnut crops. Herbicides are designed for fruits, vegetables, turf grasses and 'ornamentals'. Di Methionine is a well-known feed supplement.

EMC GROUP—French (1977)

Sales: Fr. 4,000,000,000
Employees: 11,000
Product Lines: EMC is a public company with 49% of its sales overseas, including extensive operations in West Africa. It is engaged in mining, fertilizers, animal feed, seed and agricultural implements.
Seed Activities: Operations appear to be largely through SCPA (Societé Commerciale des Potasses et de l'Azote) which sells seed, potash, agricultural equipment and binary PK fertilizers.
Other: Potash sales equal about 6.5% of total world sales. The firm is also involved in stock breeding and emphasizes its general ability to respond to requests from developing nations.

FMC—USA (1977)

Sales: US $2,373,234,000
US Fortune Rank: #103
Employees: 44,249
Product Lines: The firm has 135 production facilities in 14 countries including the USA. It has five major product lines: food and agricultural machinery and chemicals; industrial chemicals; material and natural resources handling equipment; construction and power transmission products; and, government and municipal equipment. Of total sales, US $636.7 million occur outside the USA.
Seed Activities: FMC recently purchased Seed Research Assoc. in the USA.
Other: FMC has extensive agrichemical interests including Furadan (insecticide) used on corn and rice, and Pounce (insecticide) used on cotton. Pounce is used extensively in Central America; Furadan is used on rice in South America. FMC also produces Avicel used in food and pharmaceuticals; this is manufactured in Cork, Ireland. FMC also uses seaweed farmed in the Philippines for a natural food additive in processed foods — especially in combination with milk products. Ethion and Thiodan are two other FMC insecticides. Polyram is a fungicide.

ITT — USA (1977)

Sales: US $13,145,664,000
US Fortune Rank: #11
Employees: 375,000
Product Lines: ITT is a highly diversified conglomerate operating in virtually every country. Its product line includes telecommunications equipment, publishing, forestry, insurance, bakeries, a variety of engineering products and consumer products. More than half of ITT's annual sales are derived outside of the USA.
Seed Activities: ITT recently purchased O. M. Scott and Sons — a dominant US firm in grasses; as well as Burpee Seeds, the USA's largest garden seed

retailer. Scott is engaged in marketing a variety of lawn products. ITT is also involved in forest genetics.

Other: ITT has admitted to US $11,338,000 in dubious overseas payments.

MONSANTO — USA (1977)

Sales: US $4,594,500,000
US Fortune Rank: #44
Employees: 61,519
Product Lines: Agricultural Products — Chemical Intermediates — Commercial Products — Industrial Chemicals — Plastics and Resins — Textiles. Although agricultural products contributed only US $654 million to sales, it was the largest contributor to profits. Almost US $1,200 million of sales were outside the USA.
Seed Activities: Monsanto recently purchased Farmers' Hybrid Company.
Other: Monsanto's other agricultural activities include herbicides, insecticides, a plant growth regulator, fertilizers and animal breeding stock. Lasso herbicide is used on corn in Europe and on soybeans in South America. Roundup is used on cotton, sugar cane and citrus fruits in Brazil, Scandinavian forest preserves, French vineyards, Malaysian rubber plantations and Australian cereal crops. In North America, Roundup is used to fight perennial weeds like quackgrass. Avadex is used against wild oats in wheat and grains. Machete is a rice herbicide used in Korea, Japan and Taiwan. Polaris (plant growth regulator) is used as an insecticide on cotton in the USA and Central America. Monsanto has 98 manufacturing plants in 21 non-US countries, and derives 31% of its sales abroad. It also has 76 sales offices in 42 countries. Monsanto is presently being sued for a PCB spill in the USA; and also told the US SEC of US $3,624,700 in questionable foreign payments.

OCCIDENTAL PETROLEUM—USA (1977)

Sales: US $6,017,517,000
US Fortune Rank: #27
Employees: 32,000
Product Lines: A major oil and gas company, Occidental is also engaged in industrial chemicals; plastics; metal finishing chemicals and equipment; agricultural chemicals and fertilizers.
Seed Activities: No known acquisitions but L. Wm. Teweles & Co. identifies Occidental as a major new force in plant breeding.
Other: Occidental wholly owns Hooker Chemicals which has been reorganized and expanded to handle a range of agricultural chemicals and fertilizers. The company has a major Russian fertilizer programme, as well as animal feed operations. Zoecon Corp. (a recent subsidiary) is industry leader in insect growth regulators (methonrene). Zoecon has plants in Spain, Canada and Japan, as well as the USA. Insect growth regulator is used in silk production. Zoecan had 144 US patents (added in '77) aimed at insect control — ranking it among the top 50 US pesticide patent holders. Hooker holds the patent on BHC biocide, shipped without danger warnings to the Third World from the USA.

OLIN—USA (1977)

Sales: US $1,472,500,000
US Fortune Rank: #174
Employees: 22,000
Product Lines: Olin manufactures chemicals, metals, flax-based paper, cellophane, skiing equipment, shooting weapons and bullets, and is actively involved in home building. The firm is involved in fertilizers, fungicides and seed treatment chemicals. With Royal Dutch/Shell, Olin owns North American Plant Breeders, which is involved in both seeds and seed inoculants.
Seed Activities: Olin shares ownership of North American Plant Breeders (NAPB) which breeds proprietary grains, forage, soybeans and other seeds.
Other: Olin is involved in biocides and pharmaceuticals, as well as cosmetics. Ammo-Phos is a well-known Olin fertilizer brand. Terrachlor and Terrazole are two Olin fungicides used in direct application to the soil and as seed treatment chemicals. The Company owns Winchester Rifle, Winchester and Western Ammunition, and Weaver Optical (sights). In 1978, Olin paid a fine of US $510,000 for shipping guns and ammunition to South Africa. This shipping arrangement lasted for many years according to the firm. Olin also admitted to 'false reports' relating to the environmental damage caused by its Niagara Falls, New York chemical plant — and may be fined up to US $200,000. Olin manufactures biocides in Ireland, which are exported to a world-wide market. It also has a chemical plant in Africa; and another in Venezuela.

PFIZER—USA (1977)

Sales: US $2,031,925,000
US Fortune Rank: #126
Employees; 40,200
Product Lines: Primarily a pharmaceutical/medical supply company, Pfizer also develops and markets animal health care products; plant and animal genetics; organic fine chemicals for the food, beverage and health care industries; and, consumer products such as fragrances and cosmetics. Pfizer operates 140 production facilities in 40 countries, and has extensive operations in all areas of the Third World.
Seed Activities: Pfizer has recently purchased Clemens Seed Farms, Jordan Wholesale Co., Trojan Seed Co. and Warwick Seeds. It is particularly active in corn, soybean and oat seeds.
Other: Pfizer agricultural products had world-wide sales in '77 of US $310.8 million, or 15% of corporate sales; of this, US $200 million was derived outside of the USA and Europe. Mecadox is a growth promoter for animals that has large non-US sales. Pfizer has reported US $1,665,458 in questionable foreign payments. About 57% of Pfizer sales are outside the USA.

PIONEER HI-BRED INTERNATIONAL INC.—USA (1977)

Sales: US $280,965,885
Employees: 2,138
Product Lines: Seed — Poultry — Computer Services. The company markets its products in over 100 countries.

Seed Activities: Lankhart Inc.; Lockett Inc.; and Arnold Thomas Seed Company. Regarding the US market, Pioneer has 29.3% of the hybrid corn, 15.8% of the hybrid grain sorghum, 8.3% of the alfalfa seed, 2.1% of the soybean seed, 4% of the cotton seed and a negligible percentage of the wheat seed (although it is becoming a major US producer of hybrid hard red winter wheat). In addition, Pioneer has 18.9% of the US pullet chick, 22.3% of the hatched parent stock egg layers and 1.8% of the broiler breeder parents poultry markets in the USA. The US seed market is valued at US $7.6 billion. Pioneer faces a class action law suit related to the 1970 corn leaf blight in the southern USA.

PUREX—USA (1978)
Sales: US $491,219,000
US Fortune Rank: #397
Employees: 7,100
Product Lines: Extensive consumer products; flower, vegetable and farm seeds; household cleaning agents; industrial, institutional and commercial equipment; chemicals; and, airmotive and industrial engine services.
Seed Activities: Purex has recently purchased Advanced Seeds, Ferry-Morse Seeds and Hulting Hybrids. Ferry-Morse is a major retailer of packet seeds and has extensive international sales. Purex is also involved in hybrid corn seed.
Other: Purex disclosed US $447,336 before the SEC in questionable foreign payments.

RANKS HOVIS McDOUGALL—UK (1977)
Sales: £1,107 million
Intern'l Fortune Rank: #133
Employees: 57,248
Product Lines: With a major interest in flour milling, RHM has bakeries, seeds, animal feeds, fast-food restaurants, pizza suppliers, agrichemicals and fertilizers. The company operates overseas in Australia, New Zealand, the Philippines, Indonesia, South Africa and Argentina.
Seed Activities: RHM has an extensive involvement in agroservices in the UK through county seed firms that market — among other things — seed, biocides and fertilizers. RHM Seeds was ten years old in '77 and is particularly involved in cereal seeds. RHM suggests that farmers grow half a million acres of cereals from RHM seed.
Other: RHM has developed wheat and barley identification programmes and a method of separating wild oats from wheat seed. RHM sells Superlac 10 Grazing Nuts for dairy cattle.

ROYAL DUTCH/SHELL—UK/NETH. (1977)
Sales: US $39,700,000,000
Intern'l Fortune Rank: #1
Employees: 155,000
Chemicals: RD/S claims to have the largest chemical interests of any oil company. Shell Oil had US $1.7 billion in chemical sales in '77, with fully US

$300 million of this in agrichemical sales. Among major pesticides contributing to profits are Pydrin (under license from Summitono Chemicals of Japan) for cotton crops, and Bladex for corn crops. The Canadian prairies know Shell best for Endaven and Mataven herbicides. Shell Oil and its Velsico subsidiary both have products being retested by US and Canadian government officials, following the Industrial Bio-Test Ltd. scandal including Hexakis and Methazole among others. Shell/Velsico also marketed Aldrin, Heptachlorendrin, Dieldrin and Leptophos. The pervasive spread of Dieldrin — to the point where most North Americans have traceable quantities in their bodies — has been of particular concern. Leptophos was produced in Texas solely for markets in Egypt, Indonesia and Colombia. Both human and livestock deaths were recorded in those countries; and in Texas, plant workers often became seriously ill.

Seeds: RD/S controls Nickerson Seeds Co. in the UK. Between RD/S and Nickerson, the parent entity has a massive influence on the European seed industry, with control over such large firms as Bush Johnson, International Plant Breeders and Rothwell Plant Breeders (control in the latter is shared with Ranks Hovis McDougall) in the UK market. In Holland, RD/S holds both Zwaan and Zwaanesse, as well as Broersen. RD/S has other seed companies in France, Germany, Sweden and Denmark that appear to be of considerable importance. A survey in the summer of '78 identified at least eighteen large European seed firms linked to RD/S. Some researchers suggest that RD/S dominates at least 23 European seed enterprises. RD/S is also linked with the US Olin Corporation in controlling North American Plant Breeders and Agripro.

SANDOZ—Swiss (1977)

Sales: Sw. Fr. 4,773,000,000
Intern'l Fortune Rank: #126
Employees: 35,605
Product Lines: Dyes — Pharmaceuticals — Agrichemicals — Seeds — Food Products. Ovaltine may be the firm's best known consumer product. Of total sales, 94.9% are outside Switzerland, with 27.5% in North America. Brazil and India rank in a listing of the firm's top 12 customers.
Seed Activities: Sandoz has recently purchased National-NK, Rogers Brothers and Northrup-King seed companies. Its world-wide seed sales amounted to Sw. Fr. 464 million in 1977. Sales include corn hybrid, sorghum hybrid, sunflower, soybean, alfalfa, wheat and vegetable seeds.
Other: In agrichemicals (sales = Sw. Fr. 250 million), Sandoz leases Roundup herbicide from Monsanto. It also markets Zorial, a cotton herbicide used in South and Central America. Thuricide insecticide is also used in South America. A virus preparation, Elcar, is sold in Brazil to treat its coffee and cocoa crops. French vineyards use Metoxuron-based herbicides. Eastern Europe uses Despirol insecticide extensively, while India and Pakistan make use of the Ekalux insecticide. Ekamet and Evisect insecticides are being made ready for world markets, as are Saffotin insecticide and Solican herbicide. Sandoz works closely with Ciba-Geigy: they are building a water treatment plant on the French border for their Basle, Switzerland plants; in Venezuela,

the two firms have a joint venture — Covigal SA — enabling pharmaceutical sales in the Andes Pact area; and the two Basle-based Swiss firms share a common agrichemical factory in Resende, Brazil. Sandoz also worked with Ciba-Geigy and other Swiss multinationals to quietly influence the UN 'Group of Eminent Persons' in their study of multinationals and developing countries.

TATE & LYLE—UK (1978)
Sales: £1,147 million
Intern'l Fortune Rank: #118 (1977)
Employees: 20,015
Product Lines: Agribusiness — Bulk Liquid Storage — Commodity Trading — Malting — Shipping — Starch — Sugar Refining — Sugar Production — Warehousing and Distribution. The firm has subsidiaries in 21 countries including Mozambique, Brazil, Belize, Bermuda, Ivory Coast, Zimbabwe-Rhodesia, South Africa, Guyana, Mauritius and Hong Kong.
Seed Activities: The firm recently acquired Berger & Plate seed company.
Other: Tate & Lyle also own Farrow irrigation equipment. The firm appears to have extensive agricultural interests in both Africa and the West Indies.

UNION CARBIDE—USA (1977)
Sales: US $7,036,100,000
US Fortune Rank: #21
Employees: 113,669
Product Lines: Chemicals and plastics (40% of sales); Gas-related products, metals and carbons (33% of sales); and, Consumer and specialty goods (27% of sales). Union Carbide markets via subsidiaries in 35 countries outside the USA, and derives 32% of its sales abroad. Consumer brand products include Glad garbage bags, Everready batteries and Prestone anti-freeze.
Seed Activities: Firm recently purchased Keystone Seed Company.
Other: Besides its involvement in health care products and chemical coatings for the food industry, Union Carbide is active in crop protection via Sevin (Carbaryl insecticide), Temik (aldicarb pesticide) and Weedone (herbicide). In 1977, the company bought Amchem Products Inc. from Rohr-Amchem, and substantially increased its agrichemical involvement. Amchem Products makes metalworking chemicals, herbicides, seed corn and the chemical ripening spray for Florida's 'Walter' tomatoes.

UPJOHN—USA (1977)
Sales: US $1,134,325,000
US Fortune Rank: #217
Employees: 18,830
Product Lines: Major company areas are in pharmaceuticals, medical services, chemicals, seeds and agricultural specialties. Of total sales, 37.2% were non-US — directed to 150 countries. Upjohn has manufacturing facilities in 17 countries, not including the USA and Puerto Rico. Among other nations, plants are in Argentina, Venezuela, Guatemala, Mexico, Korea and Indonesia.

117

Seed Activities: Asgrow Seeds and Associated Seeds were bought recently. Asgrow is a leading US vegetable seed company, developing and selling peas, beans and sweet corn. It also develops and markets agronomic seed: hybrid corn, hybrid sorghum and soybeans. In Florida, Asgrow also formulates and distributes agricultural chemicals and equipment. It breeds 'Pacesetter 490' tomatoes.

Other: Cobb Inc. is involved in poultry genetics. Upjohn and Asgrow are involved in a wide range of agrichemicals including: Enide (herbicide), Actidione (fungicide), Botran (fungicide) and Baam (pesticide). According to the US SEC, Upjohn made US $890,771 in dubious overseas payments. In its 1977 Annual Report, Upjohn noted that research scientists involved in health care for animals and humans work closely with plant breeders at the firm's integrated facility in Kalamazoo, Michigan.

Appendix B

Abbreviations

AAASA	—Association for the Advancement of Agricultural Sciences in Africa
ASSINSEL	—International Association of Breeders for the Protection of Breeders' Rights
CCIC	—Canadian Council for International Co-operation
CGIAR	—Consultative Group on International Agricultural Research
CIAT	—International Centre for Tropical Agriculture
CIDA	—Canadian International Development Agency
CIMMYT	—International Maize and Wheat Improvement Centre
CIP	—International Potato Centre
EEC	—European Economic Community
EPPO	—European and Mediterranean Plant Protection Organization
FAO	—Food and Agriculture Organization
FIS	—Fédération Internationale des Semences
GR/CIDS	—Genetic Resources Communications, Information and Documentation System
HRV	—High-Responding Variety
HYV	—High-Yielding Variety
IBPGR	—International Board for Plant Genetic Resources
IBT	—Industrial Bio-Test Ltd.
ICARDA	—International Centre for Agricultural Research in Dry Areas
ICDA	—International Coalition for Development Action

ICRISAT	—International Crops Research Institute for the Semi-Arid Tropics
IDRC	—International Development Research Centre
IITA	—International Institute of Tropical Agriculture
INPADOC	—International Patent Documentation Centre
IPBR	—International Plant Breeders' Rights
IRRI	—International Rice Research Institute
IS/GR	—Information Sciences/Genetic Resources Programme
ISTA	—International Seed Testing Association
NAPB	—North American Plant Breeders
NAS	—US National Academy of Sciences
NGO	—Non-Governmental Organization
NSSL	—National Seed Storage Laboratory
PBR	—Plant Breeders' Rights
PGRC	—Plant Genetic Resources of Canada
R & D	—Research and Development
SCIC	—Saskatchewan Council for International Co-operation
SEC	—US Securities and Exchange Commission
SIDP	—Seed Improvement and Development Programme
UNCTAD	—United Nations Conference on Trade and Development
UNDP	—United Nations Development Programme
UNEP	—United Nations Environment Programme
UNESCO	—United Nations Educational, Scientific and Cultural Organization
UPOV	—Union for the Protection of New Varieties of Plants
USDA	—US Department of Agriculture
WARDA	—West African Rice Development Association
WIPO	—World Intellectual Properties Organization
YUP	—Yield, Uniformity and Processing